Mr Bridge's
Quiz and
Puzzle Book

Mr Bridge's Quiz and Puzzle Book

Bernard Magee

foulsham
LONDON • NEW YORK • TORONTO • SYDNEY

foulsham

The Publishing House, Bennetts Close,
Cippenham, Berkshire, SL1 5AP, England

Copyright © 1997 Mr Bridge

ISBN 0-572-02392-8

Printed in Great Britain by Cox & Wyman Ltd, Reading

Contents

Introduction

If the aim of a good book is to entertain and instruct, then this book cannot be far off the mark. All of the problems contained herein are original, created by the author Bernard Magee. They are neatly designed to take up a page each, with the answer following immediately overleaf.

The author takes you on a trip through many of the fascinating areas of the world of bridge. Starting at the very beginning, there is a chapter of basic plays to whet your appetite; the book then moves on to a variety of notrumps and on through the forest to exotic chapters like 'Moysian' and 'Goulash'. To bring you down to earth there is a chapter, 'Wrong Contract', where you are left at the helm after some less-than-perfect auctions. Then, finally, everyone's favourite – slams.

The book includes problems for declarer, defender and bidder alike, allowing you to expand your game in all directions. The problems are set to intrigue and instruct, and are not deliberately difficult.

As a special treat, there is a puzzle at the end of each chapter with a bridge theme. There are the usual favourites, but most are specially designed for the book and the bridge players who will read it.

 **Mr Bridge**

CHAPTER ONE

Starting Up

We start with some easier hands, containing aspects of basic technique. Hold ups, endplays, safety plays, etc. All to whet your appetite.

Q

Dealer: South   Game All

```
              ♠ 5 3
              ♡ K 10 5 3
              ◇ A 7 5 3
              ♣ K Q 6
                   N
Lead = ♠K     W       E
                   S
              ♠ A 9 6
              ♡ A J 8
              ◇ K 8 6 2
              ♣ A J 3
```

South	West	North	East
1NT (15-17)	Pass	2♣	Pass
2◇	Pass	3NT	All Pass

The bidding was simple: South opened a strong notrump, and North made a Stayman enquiry for four-card majors before raising to game.

Unfortunately the defence have found your weakest suit – what can you do?

A

Dealer: South Game All

                    ♠ 5 3
                    ♡ K 10 5 3
                    ◇ A 7 5 3
                    ♣ K Q 6

♠ K Q J 7 4   ┌─────────┐   ♠ 10 8 2
♡ Q 9 4   │   N   │   ♡ 7 6 2
◇ J 9   W   │   │   E   ◇ Q 10 4
♣ 8 7 2   │   S   │   ♣ 10 9 5 4
                    └─────────┘
                    ♠ A 9 6
                    ♡ A J 8
                    ◇ K 8 6 2
                    ♣ A J 3

South	West	North	East
1NT (15-17)	Pass	2♣	Pass
2◇	Pass	3NT	All Pass

West leads the ♠K.

There are eight top winners and good chances for extra tricks in the red suits. Hearts appear to be the better option because you can guarantee an extra trick in that suit by knocking out the ♡Q.

The only danger is losing four spade tricks as well as the ♡Q. This can only happen if one defender holds five spades. So you must try to cut the defenders' communications, by holding up your ace until one of them has no spades left.

There are eight spades out, and with one holding five the other will hold three, so you must not win your ace until the third round. That done, you must still avoid West (the one with five spades) getting the lead. So finesse into East's hand, because you do not mind if he wins the trick; he can do no harm and you will have established your ninth trick.

Win the third spade and play the ♡A, followed by a small heart to the ten. When this holds cash the king; on this occasion West's queen falls, so that you now have ten tricks, to make 3NT + 1.

Notice that had you finessed the other way, West would have won and cashed his spades for one off.

Q

Dealer: South   Love All

♠ 8 3 2
♡ A 6 5
◇ A K J
♣ 10 9 5 4

```
     N
  W     E
     S
```

Lead = ♠4

♠ A 7 5
♡ 3 2
◇ Q 4 3
♣ K Q J 6 3

South	West	North	East
1NT (12-14)	Pass	3NT	All Pass

East plays the ♠Q at trick one.

Another simple auction, but this time with a weak notrump. You appear to be a point short for a 3NT contract, but hopefully your club suit will make up for that.

Again the defence have attacked a weak spot. What should you do?

A

Dealer: South   Love All

```
                    ♠ 832
                    ♡ A65
                    ◇ AKJ
                    ♣ 10954
    ♠ KJ64           ┌─────────┐        ♠ Q109
    ♡ 1097           │    N    │        ♡ KQJ84
    ◇ 9875           │ W     E │        ◇ 1062
    ♣ 72             │    S    │        ♣ A8
                     └─────────┘
                    ♠ A75
                    ♡ 32
                    ◇ Q43
                    ♣ KQJ63
```

South	West	North	East
1NT (12-14)	Pass	3NT	All Pass

West leads the ♠4 and East plays the ♠Q at trick one.

Five tricks on top but an obvious source of extra tricks (clubs). The problem is how to avoid five losers – the ♣A and four spades.

The first thought is to hold up in spades as before to break communications, but when you duck East's queen, he switches to the ♡K and you really are in trouble.

Remember, the time to think is before you play to trick one. There are two weak suits: hearts and spades; and you should analyse the spade situation before you blithely duck a round. West's lead will be fourth highest, and notice that you can see the ♠3 and ♠2 in dummy. So it looks as if West has only four spades.

You should win the lead straight away and knock out the ♣A. Whatever East now plays it matters not, the defence can take only four tricks.

Never duck for the sake of ducking, think your play through.

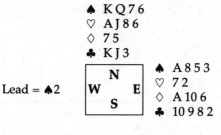

Dealer: South   Love All

```
            ♠ K Q 7 6
            ♡ A J 8 6
            ◇ 7 5
            ♣ K J 3
                              ♠ A 8 5 3
                      N       ♡ 7 2
Lead = ♠2    W         E      ◇ A 10 6
                      S       ♣ 10 9 8 2
```

South	West	North	East
1NT (15-17)	Pass	2♣	Pass
2♡	Pass	4♡	All Pass

Declarer plays the ♠6 from dummy at trick one.

One look at dummy suggests that you will need a little luck to defeat this contract – it is surprising that North did not make a slam try.

What is partner's lead? And where are your four tricks going to come from?

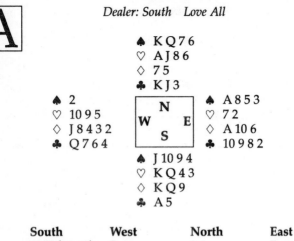

A

Dealer: South   Love All

♠ K Q 7 6
♥ A J 8 6
♦ 7 5
♣ K J 3

♠ 2
♥ 10 9 5
♦ J 8 4 3 2
♣ Q 7 6 4

♠ A 8 5 3
♥ 7 2
♦ A 10 6
♣ 10 9 8 2

♠ J 10 9 4
♥ K Q 4 3
♦ K Q 9
♣ A 5

South	West	North	East
1NT (15-17)	Pass	2♣	Pass
2♥	Pass	4♥	All Pass

Partner leads the ♠2 and declarer plays the ♠6 from dummy.

You have very little chance of getting this contract down, with partner only having a possible 3 points in his hand (dummy has 14 plus your 8 and declarer's minimum 15 = 37). The only chance is that the lead is a singleton and you can give partner two spade ruffs.

Win the ♠A and play back a spade – but which spade?

It is very important to choose the right spade. In these situations the spade you play back tells partner what to lead next – a high spade would ask for the higher non-trump suit, a low spade would ask for the lower non-trump suit. You have the ♦A so you want him to play diamonds (the higher suit), so you should play back the ♠8.

Partner ruffs the spade and obeys your signal by returning a diamond. You win and play back another spade for partner to ruff and set the contract.

Your play at trick two (the ♠8) was a suit-preference signal; without it partner would have been guessing and might well have chosen a club, following the old maxim of leading through dummy's strength.

Q

Dealer: South   Game All

```
                    ♠  A 9 5 4
                    ♡  Q J 10
                    ◇  7 3
                    ♣  A K 6 3
                         N
Lead = ♡ A       W         E
                         S
                    ♠  K J 8 2
                    ♡  9 6 5 4
                    ◇  A K
                    ♣  Q J 9
```

South	West	North	East
1NT (12-14)	Pass	2♣	Pass
2♡	Pass	3NT	Pass
4♠	All Pass		

West leads the ♡ A, ♡ K and a third heart, all following.

After a weak notrump, North uses Stayman and leaps to 3NT after South shows four hearts. For this auction North promises four spades and so South bid 4♠. 3NT would have been easier – an easy ninth trick available in spades and no need to worry about a ruff – but still, 4♠ looks pretty good after the third heart stands up.

What is the best line for ten tricks?

A

Dealer: South   Game All

```
                    ♠ A 9 5 4
                    ♡ Q J 10
                    ◇ 7 3
                    ♣ A K 6 3
    ♠ Q 10 6 3                        ♠ 7
    ♡ A K 3         ┌─────────┐       ♡ 8 7 2
    ◇ Q 8 5 4       │    N    │       ◇ J 10 9 6 2
    ♣ 10 4          │ W     E │       ♣ 8 7 5 2
                    │    S    │
                    └─────────┘
                    ♠ K J 8 2
                    ♡ 9 6 5 4
                    ◇ A K
                    ♣ Q J 9
```

South	West	North	East
1NT (12-14)	Pass	2♣	Pass
2♡	Pass	3NT	Pass
4♠	All Pass		

West leads the ♡A, ♡K and a third heart, all following.

After the first three tricks you are left with no losers outside trumps. Hence you can afford to lose a trump trick and can make a safety play in the suit. This is a play that secures the contract against most bad breaks, but might result in the loss of an overtrick if the suit breaks favourably.

Here, had you needed to avoid a spade loser, you would have cashed the ace and finessed East for the queen. Instead you make a play designed to lose just one trick when the suit breaks 4-1.

Cash the ♠K and lead a low spade towards dummy. If West follows small, insert the nine: now if East wins, then the suit is breaking 3-2 and your ace will take care of the outstanding spade; if East shows out then your ♠A will win the next round, and you will just lose the last round.

If West shows out on the second spade, take your ace and play a spade back towards the jack. East is helpless: if he plays his ♠Q you will play small and if he plays small you will win your jack. Whoever holds four spades you will always make three tricks in the suit.

Q

Dealer: North   East-West Game

```
              ♠ A K 3
              ♡ 7 4
              ◇ K Q 5
              ♣ K Q J 10 3
♠ Q J 10 8 4        N
♡ K Q 9      W          E
◇ 9 7 6             S
♣ A 9
```

South	West	North	East
		1♣	Pass
1NT	Pass	3NT	All Pass

You lead the ♠Q which declarer wins with the ♠A, partner following with the ♠9. The ♣K follows.

North has a good 18-count and is thus suitable for his jump to game. The spade lead was not massively successful, but it will take only one more round to establish the suit. Partner plays the ♣8 underneath the king and you duck, but are forced to take the next round.

What is there to think about?

(1) How many spades does partner hold?
(2) How many points does partner hold?
(3) How can you possibly take the contract off?

A

Dealer: North   East-West Game

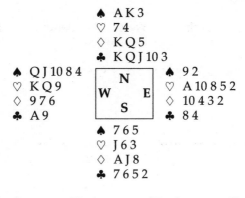

♠ A K 3
♥ 7 4
♦ K Q 5
♣ K Q J 10 3

♠ Q J 10 8 4   ♠ 9 2
♥ K Q 9   **N**   ♥ A 10 8 5 2
♦ 9 7 6   **W** **E**   ♦ 10 4 3 2
♣ A 9   **S**   ♣ 8 4

♠ 7 6 5
♥ J 6 3
♦ A J 8
♣ 7 6 5 2

South	West	North	East
		1♣	Pass
1NT	Pass	3NT	All Pass

Declarer wins your ♠Q with the ♠A, partner following with the ♠9. The ♣K follows.

(1) Partner played the ♠9 at trick one – he will generally try to tell you how many cards he holds in your suit especially when dummy is so strong. Here he has played his highest card first to show an even number (or a singleton!). He will not have four cards for that leaves South with just one and he bid 1NT in response to 1♣.

(2) South is marked with at least 6 points, so partner can only have the remaining 4 – he might have less, but to get this contract down you will need all four!

(3) You are not going to get this contract down by leading spades. Partner will be unable to lead a third spade if he wins a trick (he only has two), and you are certainly not going to win a trick. Your best hope is hearts. South did not bid hearts, so is unlikely to hold four, leaving partner with five and if he has the ace you will be able to take five tricks right away. It is your only hope.

Switch to the ♥K, and continue the suit. Partner wins the third round and cashes two more hearts taking 3NT two off.

Notice that declarer actually has nine tricks after he has knocked out the ♣A, hence the urgency for the switch.

What would you bid with the following hands after the auction:

South	West	North	East
1♡	Double	?	

(A) ♠ K Q 5 4 3
    ♡ 7 2
    ◊ J 7 5
    ♣ J 6 4

(B) ♠ K 4
    ♡ J 9 3 2
    ◊ 8 6 4
    ♣ 9 7 3 2

(C) ♠ K 4
    ♡ J 8 5 3
    ◊ A 8 6 4
    ♣ 9 7 3

(D) ♠ K 4
    ♡ Q 9 6 3
    ◊ A 8 6 4
    ♣ K 9 3

(E) ♠ K 5 3
    ♡ K 9
    ◊ Q 10 4 3
    ♣ K 10 6 4

(F) ♠ 2
    ♡ Q J 10 5 4 3
    ◊ K 10 5 4 3
    ♣ 7

What rules are there?

(1) You should stretch your raises – push a little harder to make it more difficult for the opposition.
(2) Use the 2NT response as a normal raise to 3♡.
(3) With strong hands without support you redouble.
(4) Other than the above you should bid naturally.

(A) 1♠. A nice and easy start – very natural.

(B) 2♡, a stretch raise. You do not hold enough to bid 2♡ under normal circumstances, but move one up the ladder here: from no raise to a single raise.

(C) 3♡, a stretch raise. This time you have a normal 2♡ bid, but again when there is an intervening double you should stretch your raises: from a single raise to a double raise.

(D) 2NT. Artificial, showing heart support and a raise to the three level. Because the stretch raises have swallowed up your usual 3♡ bid (see (C) above) you need a bid to show this hand-type. The reason for stretching your raises is to pre-empt the opponents; when you have a good hand yourself there is no reason to pre-empt them. Rather than stretching this normal 3♡ bid to 4♡ you bid an artificial 2NT (a hand that would normally bid 2NT starts with a redouble (see (E) below).

(E) Redouble, showing strength. You have been given an extra bid, so why not use it? You would usually respond 2NT with this hand, but you can show 9 or more points by redoubling. Perhaps you will be able to penalise the opponents when they try to bid their suit.

(F) 4♡, pre-emptive raise. With your distribution, partner has a very good chance of making game, but if he cannot manage it, the opposition are likely to be able to make a game elsewhere. It is a two-way shot.

Q

Dealer: South   Love All

<pre>
                    ♠ 9 7 6 5 3
                    ♡ A K 7
                    ◇ A J
                    ♣ A J 3
                        ┌─────────┐
                        │   N   │
    Lead = ♠4   │ W   E │
                        │   S   │
                        └─────────┘
                    ♠ A K 10 8 2
                    ♡ Q 6 4
                    ◇ 3 2
                    ♣ K 10 9
</pre>

South	West	North	East
1♠	Pass	4NT[1]	Pass
5◇	Pass	5NT[1]	Pass
6♡	Pass	6♠	All Pass

[1] normal Blackwood, for aces, then kings

North had no conventional way to show a good hand with a fit for his partner so he decided to use Blackwood immediately. When he discovered he was missing a king he decided to settle for the small slam, wisely as it turned out. His bid of 5NT confirmed that all the aces were present so if South had had an unexpected source of tricks along with good trumps he could proceed to the grand slam.

At trick one you win East's queen with your ace.

Who has the queen of clubs?

If you cannot answer that, try 'How do you make the contract?'

A

Dealer: South   Love All

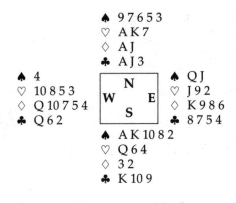

```
                    ♠ 9 7 6 5 3
                    ♡ A K 7
                    ◇ A J
                    ♣ A J 3
    ♠ 4                           ♠ Q J
    ♡ 10 8 5 3          N         ♡ J 9 2
    ◇ Q 10 7 5 4    W       E     ◇ K 9 8 6
    ♣ Q 6 2            S          ♣ 8 7 5 4
                    ♠ A K 10 8 2
                    ♡ Q 6 4
                    ◇ 3 2
                    ♣ K 10 9
```

South	West	North	East
1♠	Pass	4NT	Pass
5◇	Pass	5NT	Pass
6♡	Pass	6♠	All Pass

West led the ♠4 and declarer won East's queen with the ace.

The position of the ♣Q is simply a 50-50 guess, but you don't actually need to know where it is – you should aim for an *endplay*.

Draw trumps in two rounds, cash your heart winners, and cash the ◇ A. Now play your losing diamond. Whoever wins this diamond is *endplayed*. Let us look at their options:

(1) a *heart* return: this will allow you to discard a club from North and ruff in the South hand – you now have no club loser.
(2) a *diamond* return: this has a similar effect to a heart.
(3) a *club* return: second hand plays small and now if next hand plays the queen you win with the ace or king and your jack has become good, but if the third hand doesn't play the queen you win the trick cheaply with the jack or ten.
(4) they have no trumps.

The defender who wins the diamond has no winning options: he either gives a 'ruff and discard' or he 'opens up' the club suit. I think you will agree that 100% is better than 50%!

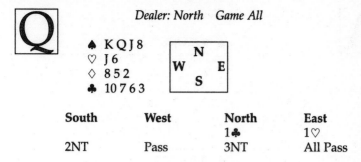

South	West	North	East
		1♣	1♡
2NT	Pass	3NT	All Pass

Both 1♣ and 2NT are natural, the latter showing 10-12 balanced. Your lead?

A

Dealer: North   Game All

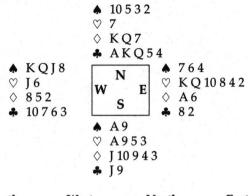

♠ 10 5 3 2
♡ 7
◊ K Q 7
♣ A K Q 5 4

♠ K Q J 8
♡ J 6
◊ 8 5 2
♣ 10 7 6 3

♠ 7 6 4
♡ K Q 10 8 4 2
◊ A 6
♣ 8 2

♠ A 9
♡ A 9 5 3
◊ J 10 9 4 3
♣ J 9

South	West	North	East
		1♣	1♡
2NT	Pass	3NT	All Pass

You have a good suit, but it is not very long and you have no entry. Unless partner holds the ♠A you will be lucky to make even three tricks. If partner does hold the ♠A you have to hope that he will find the switch later.

If the opponents are telling the truth then they have 24/25 points; adding that to your 7 points that leaves only 8 or 9 for partner. The weaker his hand the better his suit will tend to be so this suggests that a heart lead will be best, especially as you have an honour in support.

Yes, lead the top of your doubleton – the ♡J.

Declarer ducks two rounds but eventually he has to give partner the lead again with the ◊A and he will be able to cash his heart winners for two off.

On a spade lead, declarer would win the ♠A and knock out the ◊A; the defence would be kept to three tricks.

If you have a weak hand it is usually best to lead partner's suit unless you have a very good alternative. Against a suit contract, perhaps the ♠K would be better, but here, where you are trying to establish five tricks, your spades are not a good enough alternative to partner's suit.

Dealer: South   Love All

♠ 5
♡ A 10 9 8
♢ A K Q
♣ A 7 6 5 4

Lead = ♣K

```
      N
  W       E
      S
```

♠ A J 7 6 2
♡ K Q J 7
♢ 8 6 3
♣ 8

South	West	North	East
1♠	Pass	2♣	Pass
2♡	Pass	6♡!	All Pass

North had no idea what to bid at his second turn, so simply bid what he hoped his partner could make!

Can you reward his faith in you?

Dealer: South Love All

```
                ♠ 5
                ♡ A 10 9 8
                ◇ A K Q
                ♣ A 7 6 5 4
♠ K 10 4 3          N          ♠ Q 9 8
♡ 6 5         W         E       ♡ 4 3 2
◇ 10 4             S           ◇ J 9 7 5 2
♣ K Q J 10 3                    ♣ 9 2
                ♠ A J 7 6 2
                ♡ K Q J 7
                ◇ 8 6 3
                ♣ 8
```

South	West	North	East
1♠	Pass	2♣	Pass
2♡	Pass	6♡!	All Pass

West led the ♣K.

Look at your trumps, they are all high – all set for a cross-ruff. But what is the first rule of cross-ruffing? Cash the side-suit winners you need first.

To find out how many you need, count your winners – ♠A, ♣A and eight trumps – yes, you expect to make all of your trumps separately – that makes ten tricks so you need cash only two diamonds.

Win the ♣A, cash the ◇A, ◇K and ♠A. Now it is time to get down to business: spade ruff, club ruff, spade ruff, club ruff, spade ruff … etc, until you have run out of trumps! Twelve tricks.

It is lucky you counted because that third diamond winner would have been ruffed. Then a trump switch would have restricted your trick tally to eleven.

A normal Word Search to start with. Below are listed 20 conventions, one for each of the lowest 20 bids. Can you find them in the grid?

```
P C A N P R O W B I N D G E R D O U B A
G R E B E T U V E I Y A B E F S M K G F
A E E D T Y M C T A P R Q L S O U A A I
N C M C N N U A T Q K U E T E U L K M V
I A Z U I V T N E U S T R N I T I S B E
O N M B L S I F R N U O W W N H N P L C
U A Y Y F T I L M O N F B O A A D L I A
X P U X A V I O I G U L A I R F L O N R
B E N V A T K C N A M Y A T S R S F G D
E E D E A R S O O D Z N V T U I T A O M
D O T R B T T D R L M E A E Q C M P K A
O O T R A R R I R L O M R R G A J R R J
O A A R U O E T O A M U F P E N H I E O
W N M M A P R T A Z C T R Z R T C D T R
K D P O L N K A K L X E A E E E R A N P
C Y B E K I S L I T B X V F D X E T I T
A A D A P P E F G R E B E I I A R M L O
L A U S U N U W E T G T L V F S T I P R
B E L A R N K G E R B A L E D D C I S T
B L A C U E B I D K I N D L B C Z Y A T
```

1♣	PRECISION	3♣	FIVE CARD STAYMAN
1♢	BETTER MINOR	3♢	FLINT
1♡	FIVE CARD MAJOR	3♡	TRANSFER
1♠	CANAPE	3♠	PREEMPT
1NT	STRONG NOTRUMP	3NT	GAMBLING
2♣	STAYMAN	4♣	GERBER
2♢	MULTICOLOURED	4♢	SOUTH AFRICAN TEXAS
2♡	FLANNERY	4♡	CUEBID
2♠	WEAK TWO	4♠	SPLINTER
2NT	UNUSUAL	4NT	BLACKWOOD

```
P C A N P R O W B I N D G E R D O U B A
G R E B E T U V E I Y A B E F S M K G F
A E E D T Y M C T A P R Q L S O U A A I
N C M C N N U A T Q K U E T E U L K M V
I A Z U I V T N E U S T R N I T I S B E
O N M B L S I F R N U O W W N H N P L C
U A Y Y F T I L M O N F B O A A D L I A
X P U X A V I O I G U L A I R F L O N R
B E N V A T K C N A M Y A T S R S F G D
E E D E A R S O O D Z N V T U I T A O M
D O T R B T T D R L M E A E Q C M P K A
O O T R A R R I R L O M R R G A J R R J
O A A R U O E T O A M U F P E N H I E O
W N M M A P R T A Z C T R Z R T C D T R
K D P O L N K A K L X E A E E E R A N P
C Y B E K I S L I T B X V F D X E T I T
A A D A P P E F G R E B E I I A R M L O
L A U S U N U W E T G T L V F S T I P R
B E L A R N K G E R B A L E D D C I S T
B L A C U E B I D K I N D L B C Z Y A T
```

CHAPTER 2
1NT

There is a large choice for opening 1NT bids, from the 10-12 mini notrump to the super-strong 17-19 (and some even stretch above and below these!). Whichever range you use, if you end up where you started (in 1NT) the contract is sure to be difficult.

It is not just the declaring, but the defending too that is difficult – so much to think about, so many tricks to find.

All these hands are played in 1NT, spanning all the ranges, some in defence and some as declarer.

Q

Dealer: South   Love All

```
            ♠ A K 7 4
            ♡ K 9 7 2
            ◇ 8 5
            ♣ 10 7 3
```

Lead = ♣2

```
            ♠ Q 8 6
            ♡ A 5 3
            ◇ Q 9 7 6
            ♣ Q 9 4
```

South	West	North	East
1NT (10-12)	All Pass		

East wins the lead with the ♣A and returns the ♣J. Your queen wins.

What a horrible hand – did you really open the bidding on that! Well if you will bid them, then you will have to play them!

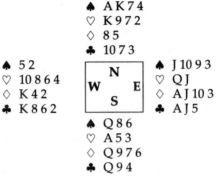

♠ A K 7 4
♡ K 9 7 2
◇ 8 5
♣ 10 7 3

♠ 5 2   ♠ J 10 9 3
♡ 10 8 6 4   ♡ Q J
◇ K 4 2   ◇ A J 10 3
♣ K 8 6 2   ♣ A J 5

♠ Q 8 6
♡ A 5 3
◇ Q 9 7 6
♣ Q 9 4

South	West	North	East
1NT (10-12)	All Pass		

East wins his partner's ♣2 lead with the ♣A and returns the ♣J. Your queen wins.

You cannot afford to establish a trick for the defence, for they are in the same situation as you, looking for their seventh trick? The lead is surely from a four-card suit and so the best thing to do is to carry on with their suit. Allowing the defence to take their suit in these situations can have various side effects, one of which can be seen here. What would you discard as East on the fourth club? A spade and a heart would cost a trick, so he actually has to discard from his best suit. Not an easy thing to do!

Suppose the defence avoid all the hazards: East discards a low diamond and West switches to a heart, say. Win the ♡K in dummy (noting the fall of an honour) and lead the ◇8 (now a singleton), covered by the ◇J and ◇Q (you are safe for the 976 still constitutes a stop).

West will win and continue hearts which you can win in hand. Now, if your card-reading skills are really up to it you will play on diamonds and get home, but more likely you will fall back on what was your best genuine chance from the start – a 3-3 spade break. Unfortunately you finish one off, but a good one off!

Notice how important it is to take your time – any defender who can get half of the defences to 1NT correct is a fine player indeed.

Q

Dealer: South   Game All

                    ♠ 7 3
                    ♡ Q 5 2
                    ♢ 10 9 6 3
                    ♣ A K 5 2

    ♠ A J 5 4   N
    ♡ A J 8   W   E
    ♢ A Q 8 4   S
    ♣ 6 3

South	West	North	East
1NT (11-13)	Double	Pass[1]	Pass
Redouble[1]	All Pass		

[1] pass forced opener to redouble

Your ♠4 lead goes to partner's ten and declarer's king. Now come the ♣A and ♣K and a third club to partner's queen. Your discard? Your plan?

This system of wriggling from 1NT is quite common with club and tournament players; it forces any doubled 1NT opening to become redoubled! This is usually so that responder with a weak hand can show various combinations of four-card suits, but when he wants to play in 1NT he simply passes the redouble. It means that once 1NT is doubled you are probably not in for a flat board!

It does increase the pressure too, for of course you are now playing for a game bonus.

A

Dealer: South   Game All

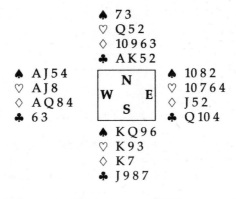

```
              ♠ 7 3
              ♡ Q 5 2
              ◇ 10 9 6 3
              ♣ A K 5 2
  ♠ A J 5 4          ♠ 10 8 2
  ♡ A J 8      N     ♡ 10 7 6 4
  ◇ A Q 8 4  W   E   ◇ J 5 2
  ♣ 6 3          S   ♣ Q 10 4
              ♠ K Q 9 6
              ♡ K 9 3
              ◇ K 7
              ♣ J 9 8 7
```

South	West	North	East
1NT (11-13)	Double	Pass	Pass
Redouble	All Pass		

Your ♠4 lead goes to partner's ten and declarer's king. Now come the ♣A and ♣K and a third club to partner's queen.

Your spades are not very good, so there might be a better continuation than that suit. Looking at dummy your diamonds are unlikely to pull their full weight, but it may be correct to switch to them. Partner can have only one or two more points to go with his ♣Q so this entry is precious. To suggest he chooses between diamonds and spades you have to make a clear signal. Discard the ◇8, encouraging the suit.

If he holds four spades and two diamonds, he should work out that spades are better, because he may well get another entry on the last round of spades to lead diamonds. But in this case he should fire back a diamond.

So, after the ♣Q, a diamond to the queen, then the ◇A (dropping the king), and a diamond to the jack, it is time for a spade through declarer's remaining honour. Two spades, one club, one heart and three diamonds = one down = +400. Nice work.

As suggested, defences to 1NT are precarious at the best of times so clear signals are essential, especially when the 1NT you are defending happens to be a game contract!

Dealer: South   Game All

```
                    ♠ 8 7 2
                    ♡ Q 7 6
                    ◇ K 4 2
                    ♣ 10 6 3 2
   ♠ K J 4 3       ┌─────────┐
   ♡ 10 9          │    N    │
   ◇ A J 8 6       │ W     E │
   ♣ A Q 7         │    S    │
                   └─────────┘
```

South	West	North	East
1NT (12-14)	Double	All Pass	

You lead the ♠3 which runs to partner's nine and declarer's queen. Declarer plays the ♣K which you win.

Dummy is a welcome sight and your lead seems to have had some success. You certainly look favourite to beat 1NT – is there something to look out for?

Dealer: South   Game All

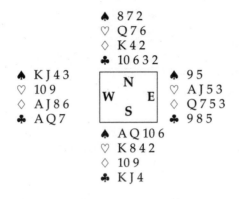

A

```
              ♠ 8 7 2
              ♡ Q 7 6
              ◇ K 4 2
              ♣ 10 6 3 2
  ♠ K J 4 3         N          ♠ 9 5
  ♡ 10 9      W         E      ♡ A J 5 3
  ◇ A J 8 6        S           ◇ Q 7 5 3
  ♣ A Q 7                      ♣ 9 8 5
              ♠ A Q 10 6
              ♡ K 8 4 2
              ◇ 10 9
              ♣ K J 4
```

South	West	North	East
1NT (12-14)	Double	All Pass	

You lead the ♠3 which runs to partner's nine and declarer's queen. Declarer plays the ♣K which you win.

Declarer has shown up with 10 points already – ♠AQ and ♣KJ – so you know that dummy has only one entry (partner will take care of the ♡Q). You should not take any chances – lead a diamond. If declarer holds the ◇Q then partner will hold the ♡A and ♡K and you will be able to generate seven tricks – two clubs and two hearts to go with two spades and one diamond or one spade and two diamonds.

As it is, with partner holding the ◇Q, you knock out declarer's entry right away, and he has nowhere to go for tricks. You will take three diamonds, two clubs, and at least one trick in each major, with good chances of taking 1NT more than one down.

Declarer's spade play was clever as it gave you a chance to go wrong. Some defenders might have continued spades straight away putting declarer in the driving seat to make three spades, two clubs, a diamond and a heart.

Dealer: South   Love All

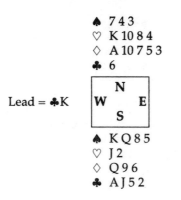

♠ 7 4 3
♡ K 10 8 4
◇ A 10 7 5 3
♣ 6

Lead = ♣K

♠ K Q 8 5
♡ J 2
◇ Q 9 6
♣ A J 5 2

South	**West**	**North**	**East**
1NT (13-15)	Double	Redouble	All Pass

You duck West's ♣K lead and he switches to the ♡3.

West's double was said to show 15 or more points. North was quite proud of his hand and so redoubled to increase the stakes to game. As always, when these kind of shenanigans take place you hold the weakest hand possible – a miserable 13-count.

Well, can you make this unexpected game?

A

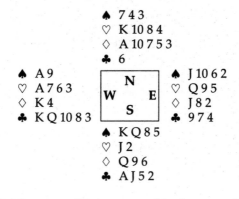

Dealer: South   Love All

```
              ♠ 7 4 3
              ♡ K 10 8 4
              ◇ A 10 7 5 3
              ♣ 6
♠ A 9              N              ♠ J 10 6 2
♡ A 7 6 3      W       E          ♡ Q 9 5
◇ K 4              S              ◇ J 8 2
♣ K Q 10 8 3                      ♣ 9 7 4
              ♠ K Q 8 5
              ♡ J 2
              ◇ Q 9 6
              ♣ A J 5 2
```

South	West	North	East
1NT (13-15)	Double	Redouble	All Pass

You duck West's ♣K lead and he switches to the ♡3.

West is favourite to have the ♡A. This is not a certainty but if East holds the ♡A he is unlikely to hold much else.

Playing the ♡K looks right; even when it loses to the ace you will still have a few chances.

As it is you win the ♡K and play a diamond to the nine. West wins his king, ducking is no good for you can simply duck the next diamond. He continues with a heart to East's queen and a club to your ace. Now come four diamonds, discarding spades from hand. Finally a spade to your queen establishes a seventh trick while still holding a heart and a club guard. However West has discarded, he must be left with a loser to play to you at trick thirteen.

West was unlikely to have underled both ace and queen of hearts because if he was going to broach the suit he would more likely lead the queen from such a holding.

If you had ducked the first heart then East would have won and returned a club. You take your ace but cannot establish diamonds without letting East in to play a second club through.

Q

Dealer: South Love All

♠ 8 5 2
♡ 8 6 2
♢ Q J 10 4
♣ Q 9 5

Lead = ♡K

	N	
W		E
	S	

♠ K 7 4
♡ A 9 5
♢ K 6 5
♣ A 8 6 3

South	West	North	East
1NT (14-16)	Pass	Pass	Double[1]
All Pass			

[1] protective, 13+

You duck the ♡K lead and West continues with the ♡Q which you also duck, East following with the ♡3 and ♡4. West now switches to the ♠3 on which East plays the ♠Q.

Playing against the stronger notrump openings it is very dangerous to play 'protective' doubles, but it seems that some players just cannot abide letting their opponents play undisturbed below two-of-a-major.

So here you are, playing in a doubled contract, and unfortunately they have caught you on a bad day for your 1NT opening was extremely minimum – although it is made up of aces and kings there is little 'meat' to the hand.

Can you prevail after the opponents have attacked both your weak suits?

Dealer: South   Love All

```
                          ♠ 852
                          ♡ 862
                          ◇ QJ10 4
                          ♣ Q95
         ♠ J963          ┌─────────┐        ♠ AQ10
         ♡ KQJ10         │    N    │        ♡ 743
         ◇ 872           │  W   E  │        ◇ A93
         ♣ 10 4          │    S    │        ♣ KJ72
                         └─────────┘
                          ♠ K74
                          ♡ A95
                          ◇ K65
                          ♣ A863
```

South	West	North	East
1NT (14-16)	Pass	Pass	Double
All Pass			

You duck the ♡K lead and West continues with the ♡Q which you also duck, East following with the ♡3 and ♡4. West now switches to the ♠3 on which East plays the ♠Q.

From East's cards on the hearts, it appears that it is West who holds four cards in the suit. Why has he switched? Most likely because he has no outside entry.

East will hold most of the remaining points (West having already shown five), notably the ♠A, ◇A and ♣K. Your only real hope is that West holds four cards in spades as well as hearts and that you can therefore restrict the defence to four winners in the majors. To do this you certainly have to duck East's cunning ♠Q.

East then switches back to hearts, which is a good sign. You win and play on diamonds. East takes the third round, then cashes the ♠A followed by another spade. You now have to play clubs, but that is easy because you know East has the ♣K. So lead a small club and cover West's card. That is, if West plays small insert the ♣9; if West plays the ♣10 cover with the queen. East has to win and return another club but you simply let this club run to dummy and claim your contract.

This line fails when West turns up with both the ♣J and ♣10, but it is certainly your best chance.

Q

Dealer: South   Game All

```
              ♠ 7 6 5
              ♡ 10 8 3
              ◇ A J 9 2
              ♣ 10 6 3
♠ A J 9 4 2        ┌─────────┐
♡ 7 6              │    N    │
◇ K Q 4 3         │ W     E │
♣ 8 2              │    S    │
                   └─────────┘
```

South	**West**	**North**	**East**
1NT (15-17)	Double[1]	All Pass	

[1] spades and another suit

You lead the ♠4 to the ten and king. Next comes the ◇6 to the ◇Q, ◇2 and ◇5.

It is rare to have a hand that wants to make a penalty double of a strong notrump, so many players in the competitive game are switching the meaning of this double to some sort of take-out: here it shows spades and another suit.

Partner has decided to make a penalty pass on borderline values by the look of dummy, perhaps he expected you to hold an extra point or two.

The lead seems to have been relatively successful, partner's ten being a key card. Now all you need is an entry to his hand. Is it just a guess?

A

Dealer: South   Game All

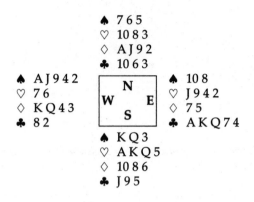

You lead the ♠4 to the ten and king. Next comes the ◇6 to the ◇Q, ◇2 and ◇5.

This one is subtle, but you have only one chance, so let's see if you can take it. Where was the signal? How many diamonds does partner have? Do we care?

Surely partner knows the situation and wants to tell you something before declarer has seven tricks? Partner will not give you count on the diamond, he will tell you which suit to lead next. So now you know where to look for the signal, it is time to decipher it.

Partner played the ◇5 – is this high or low? Well, you hold the ◇3 and ◇4, and dummy holds the ◇2, so it is definitely low. A low card asks for the low suit. Thus you have your answer.

Switch to the ♣8. Partner takes his five club tricks and then plays a spade giving you four more spade tricks – making ten in total! Yes, you take declarer four off for +1100! A heart switch does not quite have the same effect – seven tricks for declarer and –180.

A subtle signal, but a rather important one.

Declarer's line was not absurd, he was trying to sneak a diamond trick before cashing hearts. When West went up with the queen, South reasoned that with no signal West would have no idea which suit to play. He had not reckoned with your defence.

Dealer: South   Game All

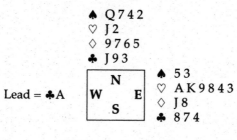

Lead = ♣A

South	West	North	East
1NT (16-18)	All Pass		

Your partner follows his ♣A with the king, queen and ten of clubs. How do you signal, and how do you play?

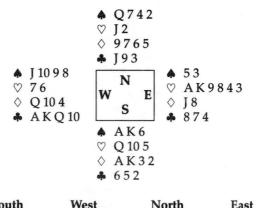

Dealer: South   Game All

A

```
                    ♠ Q 7 4 2
                    ♡ J 2
                    ◇ 9 7 6 5
                    ♣ J 9 3
    ♠ J 10 9 8            N           ♠ 5 3
    ♡ 7 6          W           E      ♡ A K 9 8 4 3
    ◇ Q 10 4              S          ◇ J 8
    ♣ A K Q 10                       ♣ 8 7 4
                    ♠ A K 6
                    ♡ Q 10 5
                    ◇ A K 3 2
                    ♣ 6 5 2
```

South	West	North	East
1NT (16-18)	All Pass		

Your partner follows his ♣A with the king, queen and ten of clubs.

You should certainly signal for a heart, and the easiest discard to that end is a high heart (the ♡9). Partner listens and plays the ♡7. Now what? Partner's ♡7 looks like a doubleton, so your hearts are not running – should you cash your top hearts or duck?

You are trying to take this contract down and you have six tricks so far. You need a seventh. If partner has a king in spades or diamonds he will make this, and so ducking a heart does little harm. But without a king, taking the first heart might be detrimental.

Here declarer has five top tricks and an easy sixth establishable in hearts. If you win your top hearts and play a third, partner will be left with an impossible discard. Squeezed between spades and diamonds he will have to give declarer a seventh trick.

If you take just one heart trick and switch, declarer wins and plays a heart himself. You cannot win this or partner is squeezed as above; but ducking leaves partner without a heart and declarer can establish a third diamond trick without the danger of a second heart loser.

Declarer may well guess wrong anyway and play for a 3-3 break in spades, but you should not give him the chance to guess right. If you duck partner's heart switch declarer has nowhere to go for his seventh trick.

Dealer: East   North-South Game

```
              ♠ J 10 9
              ♡ J 7 5 4
              ◇ K 10 9
              ♣ 10 9 6
                 ┌─────────┐
                 │    N    │
  Lead = ♣J      │ W     E │
                 │    S    │
                 └─────────┘
              ♠ A K 5 2
              ♡ A Q 2
              ◇ A Q 8
              ♣ 8 3 2
```

South	West	North	East
			Pass
1NT (17-19)	Double	All Pass	

Believe it or not, but some people do play their 1NT opening this strong.

Dummy looks good, but it is not long before West has cashed six clubs. What are your discards and what is your plan?

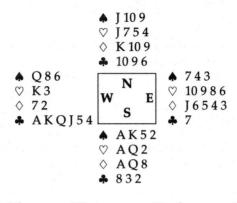

A

Dealer: East   North-South Game

♠ J 10 9
♡ J 7 5 4
◇ K 10 9
♣ 10 9 6

♠ Q 8 6   ♠ 7 4 3
♡ K 3   ♡ 10 9 8 6
◇ 7 2   ◇ J 6 5 4 3
♣ A K Q J 5 4   ♣ 7

♠ A K 5 2
♡ A Q 2
◇ A Q 8
♣ 8 3 2

South	West	North	East
			Pass
1NT (17-19)	Double	All Pass	

West leads the ♣J and follows with five more winners in the suit.

You need to keep as many options open as possible. You can only take one finesse because you have just one entry to dummy.

Spades offer a much better chance than hearts assuming you forgo the finesse, so you should play for the ♠Q to drop in two rounds, and failing that take the heart finesse. The defenders might feel some pressure themselves in the interim.

So in hand you keep ♠AK ♡AQ ◇AQ8 and in dummy ♠J109 ♡J ◇K109.

Now you win the diamond switch in hand, cash the ♠AK and then your diamonds finishing in dummy. With two cards left dummy holds the ♠J and ♡J and you hold the ♡AQ.

Now comes the crunch: with just the six clubs and little outside, West would probably have kept quiet in the hope that at his next turn his opponents might have bid to 3NT!

No, West is surely favourite to hold both ♠Q and ♡K in which case these must be his last two cards. So you simply cash the ♡A felling West's king and take the last trick with the ♡Q.

Q	South	West	North	East
	1NT	Pass	?	

A common situation, responding to the 1NT opening, but how strong is the notrump? The opening is one of two:

(i) Strong notrump (15-17)

(ii) Weak notrump (12-14)

I am sure we all tend to favour one or the other, but here you must answer for both. You are playing red-suit transfers and Stayman.

(A) ♠ K J 5 4
♡ K J 5 4 3
◇ 10 7 6
♣ 4

(B) ♠ 8 3 2
♡ 7 2
◇ 6 3
♣ A K 9 8 6 4

(C) ♠ A 3 2
♡ 7 4 2
◇ 6
♣ A K 9 8 7 6

(D) ♠ K 4 3 2
♡ 5
◇ A Q 7 6 5
♣ Q 3 2

(A) (i) 2◇ transfer to hearts followed by 2♠.
This shows the values for a raise to 2NT and 4-5 shape in the majors. Stayman followed by 2♡ over 2◇ shows a weak hand with 4-5 shape (see below).

(ii) 2♣ Stayman followed by 2♡ if partner responds 2◇.
This shows a weak take-out hand with 4-5 shape.

(B) (i) 3NT.
You have the values for a raise to 2NT, but this is a hand that should be played in 1NT or 3NT, for the outcome will invariably depend on the club suit coming in. Because you hold the ace-king, declarer will be able to duck once and still be odds on for five tricks in the suit even when he holds a small doubleton. Thus you should bid game.

(ii) Pass.
Not nearly enough for game but, holding at least two tricks for partner in notrumps, it is unnecessary to make a weakness take-out into clubs (bid 2♣ then 3♣).

(C) (i) 3♣.
Forcing to game with six clubs, with a view to a slam, or perhaps 5♣ if one suit is poorly stopped.

(ii) 3NT.
Too weak for 3♣, but much too strong simply to invite game. 3NT is the best option. There might be a suit wide open, but don't give the defenders any idea which one.

(D) (i) 2♣ Stayman followed by 3◇.
Forcing to game with five diamonds and at least one four-card major. Over the 2◇ response you have two choices – 3NT or 3◇. 3NT may give the defence no clues as to the lead, but maybe West knows what to lead anyway. 3◇ is either slam oriented or shows some worry about 3NT; if you have a good fit and a hole in the hearts 5◇ might prove easier, so why not give yourself that chance?

(ii) 2♣ Stayman followed by 2NT.
Invitational with at least one four-card major. You are not strong enough to mention diamonds so simply invite in notrumps.

Below are 20 bridge terms. Can you work out what they are?

1. ESSENIF

2. AAAAA EBONY

3. REX2
   TRICK

4. ENCOURAGING
   DISCOURAGING

5. [[CHOICE]]

6. MTWTFSSBIDBID

7. VERraiseTED

8. DART CHANGE

9. **DOWN DOWN**

10. TAX24KE

11. REDGREENBROWN◇ ◇

12. ◇ ♡ED
    CALL

13. AK – A

14. MENAMENA

15. SEQU / ENCE

16. RUFF
    →

17. 144
    BID

18. PLATHROWY

19. ELIMINATI

20. D
    L
    O
    H

1. Backward finesse
2. Five Ace Blackwood
3. Redoubled overtrick
4. High encouraging, low discouraging
5. Restricted choice
6. Weak two bid
7. Inverted minor raise
8. Arrow switch
9. Two down doubled
10. Double for take-out
11. Multicoloured Two Diamonds
12. Two-suited overcall
13. Ace from ace-king
14. Double menace
15. Broken sequence
16. Underruff
17. Gross overbid
18. Throw-in play
19. Partial elimination
20. Hold up

CHAPTER 3
Four Spades

Four of a major is one of the more common contracts we find ourselves in. So here is a chapter of spade games to wrestle with.

Q

Dealer: South   Love All

♠ 7 4
♡ J 5 2
◇ J 4
♣ Q 10 8 6 3 2

Lead = ♣A

```
    N
W       E
    S
```

♠ A K Q J 9 5 2
♡ A K 8
◇ Q 8
♣ 7

South	West	North	East
2♠[1]	Pass	2NT[1]	Pass
4♠	All Pass		

[1] strong and forcing, with negative response

West continues with a second club on which dummy plays the ♣Q and East the ♣K.

You have nine tricks on top. Any ideas for a tenth?

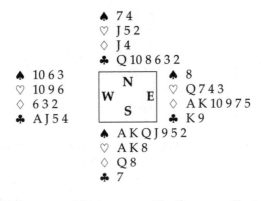

Dealer: South   Love All

A

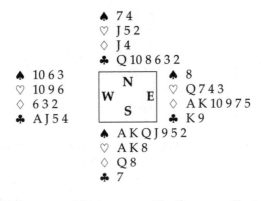

	South	West	North	East
	2♠	Pass	2NT	Pass
	4♠	All Pass		

West leads the ♣A and continues with a second club on which dummy plays the ♣Q and East the ♣K.

This is one of the problems with strong hands – you show your nine tricks, but partner fails to supply one to go with them! Well, let us see about that.

The most obvious chance is a queen singleton or doubleton in hearts, but that is not good odds. There is one extra chance which takes advantage of dummy's trump length!

Draw one round of trumps and hope for a partial elimination by exiting in diamonds.

As luck would have it, East wins the diamond and cashes another, but is now endplayed; a diamond gives a ruff and discard, and a heart can be run to dummy's jack.

It would be unwise to cash one heart first, hoping for a singleton queen (a supposed extra chance) because there are six other singleton hearts and, on the occasion that they turn up, East's heart exit will not give a trick away because his partner will be able to ruff.

Q

Dealer: North   Game All

                    ♠ K Q 9 7
                    ♡ A 7
                    ◇ A 7 6 4
                    ♣ K 6 3

        ♠ 3 2
        ♡ 10 8 4 2   N
        ◇ Q J 9   W   E
        ♣ 10 7 5 4   S

South	West	North	East
		1NT (15-17)	2♡
4♠	All Pass		

Your length in partner's suit persuades you that there is little chance of establishing a trick there so you choose instead to lead the ♣7. A very unsavoury dummy hits the table – four-card spade support and a doubleton heart. Your lead runs to partner's jack which holds the trick. Back comes a trump.

Where are your thoughts? Are you up to defeating 4♠?

A

Dealer: North   Game All

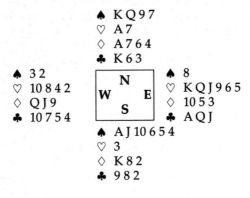

♠ K Q 9 7
♡ A 7
◇ A 7 6 4
♣ K 6 3

♠ 3 2
♡ 10 8 4 2
◇ Q J 9
♣ 10 7 5 4

♠ 8
♡ K Q J 9 6 5
◇ 10 5 3
♣ A Q J

♠ A J 10 6 5 4
♡ 3
◇ K 8 2
♣ 9 8 2

South	West	North	East
		1NT (15-17)	2♡
4♠	All Pass		

Your lead of the ♣7 runs to partner's jack which holds the trick. Back comes a trump.

You found a good lead, attacking declarer's weak point, but that is not enough, you need one more entry to defeat this contract. Easy enough, you think, because you can win the third round of diamonds.

After drawing two rounds of trumps declarer plays a heart, you follow low and are surprised to see declarer insert the ♡7. Partner has to win and now declarer is ready for anything – a diamond is taken by the king, after which comes the ◇A, ♡A discarding a diamond, and then a diamond ruff, establishing the thirteenth diamond, for declarer's tenth trick.

You had done some thinking, but not quite enough – you must insert one of your higher hearts on the first round to rescue partner. This high heart forces declarer to win his ace and try the effect of leading the ♡7, but partner casually ducks and declarer is left with a number of losing options. Eventually you will get in to play a second club through dummy, finishing off the job you started at trick one.

There are many ways to bid to game, using many different bidding techniques. Most of the hands below want to bid 4♠ in some fashion or other, but what is the first move you would make on the hands?

Your partner opens 1♠ which shows a five-card major and the next hand passes. The vulnerability is Love All.

(A)   ♠ K Q 4 3
      ♡ K Q 4 3
      ◊ 4
      ♣ K 9 4 3

(B)   ♠ 10 9 4 3 2
      ♡ 4 3
      ◊ 10 9 8 7 4 3
      ♣ —

(C)   ♠ K Q 4 3
      ♡ 4 3
      ◊ A J 10 4 3
      ♣ A 4

Partner holds:

♠ A J 8 7 6
♡ A 8
◇ K Q 5
♣ 7 6 5

(A) 4◇ You hold four-card support and enough points for game. You obviously want to bid 4♠ but do not want to waste all that space in case partner has a good hand. You have two other choices: the *Delayed Game Raise* (DGR) – a technique which involves bidding a second suit and then jumping to game in opener's suit (see (C) below); or a *splinter bid*. A splinter bid is a very simple bidding tool which uses the basically redundant double jump-shift response to show shortage in the suit bid and primary support (at least four cards) for partner. So here 4◇ shows your hand neatly and helps partner evaluate his hand. With the hand above partner would quickly sign off, holding the wasted ◇KQ opposite your singleton and no extra values. Swap his diamonds and clubs and he would be very interested, choosing instead to cue-bid 4♡. Do not be tempted to bid 4NT because that might take you too high. 5♠ is certainly too high on this hand.

(B) 4♠ Yes, really! If you cannot make game with your ten-card fit and wonderful distribution, then surely your opponents will be able to. 4♠ is not an encouraging bid – it tells partner that this is where you think he should be playing, not on point count, but on shape and fit. At the table the next hand doubled and partner wrapped up ten tricks for +590.

(C) 2◇ The Delayed Game Raise. Again you have the points for game, and you know what suit you want to be trumps, but there is no hurry; take your time and bid out your hand. The DGR is a technique which involves bidding a second suit and then jumping to game in opener's suit to show 12-16 points and primary spade support (four or more cards). Here, partner rebids 2♠ and you can jump to 4♠. Another way of showing a DGR when partner simply rebids his suit is to make a jump bid in a new suit as a cue-bid – here 4♣. This makes things much easier for partner and he can easily find a route to the good slam. Over 4♠ it is less easy because of his weakness in clubs, but he might still go on because of his good fit for your suit.

Q

Dealer: East   Game All

♠ J 10 5 4 3
♡ A Q 6
◇ A Q 6
♣ K J

Lead = ♣3

```
      N
  W       E
      S
```

♠ A K Q 9 6 2
♡ 4 2
◇ 5 4 3
♣ 9 4

South	West	North	East
			1NT (12-14)
2♠	Pass	4♠	All Pass

North held a rather good hand opposite your overcall, but with the red-suit kings likely to be offside he put any slam ambitions aside and bid straight to game.

You put in the ♣J and collect East's ace, another club comes back.

With both finesses destined for failure is there any recourse?

A

Dealer: East   Game All

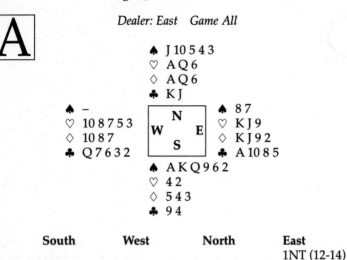

```
                    ♠ J 10 5 4 3
                    ♡ A Q 6
                    ◇ A Q 6
                    ♣ K J
        ♠ –                          ♠ 8 7
        ♡ 10 8 7 5 3        N        ♡ K J 9
        ◇ 10 8 7      W         E    ◇ K J 9 2
        ♣ Q 7 6 3 2        S        ♣ A 10 8 5
                    ♠ A K Q 9 6 2
                    ♡ 4 2
                    ◇ 5 4 3
                    ♣ 9 4
```

South	West	North	East
			1NT (12-14)
2♠	Pass	4♠	All Pass

West leads the ♣3. You put in the ♣J and collect East's ace. Another club comes back.

You draw trumps and can count nine tricks. All you need to do is put East on lead, whilst keeping your tenaces intact and you will generate a tenth. In order to maximise your chances of doing this it is best to start with the suit in which you have a doubleton, so that you have a little more control over who will be on lead.

Start with the ♡4. If West plays low then you play low. East is forced to win and is endplayed.

If West plays the ♡10, win your ace, cross to hand with a trump and play another heart, covering West's card. East wins his heart trick and plays his only safe exit card, another heart. If this is a high heart, simply discard a diamond from hand and leave East on lead; if East plays a low card, you ruff and turn to diamonds by playing low from both hands, hoping that East holds KJ10 in the suit.

On this hand West does indeed insert the ♡10. You win your ace and, as planned, cross to hand to lead another heart to the ♡8, ♡Q and ♡K. Now East plays the ♡9 (having thrown the ♡J beneath your ace). But you know that the nine is the highest heart left and you discard a diamond from hand, forcing East to give you your tenth trick.

Dealer: South   Love All

```
                    ♠ J 10 7 3
                    ♡ K 9 6 4 2
                    ◇ K 8
                    ♣ Q 9
    ♠ Q              ┌─────────┐
    ♡ A Q 5          │    N    │
    ◇ Q 7 3          │ W     E │
    ♣ J 10 8 7 3 2   │    S    │
                     └─────────┘
```

South	West	North	East
1♠	2♣	3♠	Pass
4♠	All Pass		

You lead the ♣J which is won by the queen in dummy, partner following with the four. Declarer then runs the ♠J to your queen. What next?

Dealer: South   Love All

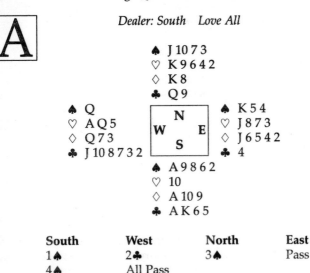

♠ J 10 7 3
♡ K 9 6 4 2
◇ K 8
♣ Q 9

♠ Q
♡ A Q 5
◇ Q 7 3
♣ J 10 8 7 3 2

♠ K 5 4
♡ J 8 7 3
◇ J 6 5 4 2
♣ 4

♠ A 9 8 6 2
♡ 10
◇ A 10 9
♣ A K 6 5

South	West	North	East
1♠	2♣	3♠	Pass
4♠	All Pass		

Your ♣J lead is won by the queen in dummy, partner following with the four. Declarer then runs the ♠J to your queen.

An important thing to remember is that declarer is not always right. Partner's most likely trump holding, given declarer's play, is Axx, in which case you need just one ruff to go with the ♠Q and the two aces. But here declarer has made a bad error. He should simply have cashed the ♠A, happy to lose two trumps and the ♡A.

Instead he has given you an easy chance to take the contract down. The message is – do not be lazy and assume you need only one ruff. Return the ♣10. Your partner will ruff and return a heart (your high club signals for the higher suit). You win your ace and return a third club which your partner can ruff with his ♠K.

Books on defence often say that you should make things easy for partner, and here you might cash your ♡A and then give partner the one ruff he needs to go with the ♠A as nothing can go wrong this way. But here your ♡A is not going to disappear so you can afford to cater for declarer's error.

Q

Dealer: South   Love All

♠ A 10 5 4
♡ –
◇ Q 7 3
♣ K 10 9 8 4 3

Lead = ◇ 4

	N	
W		E
	S	

♠ K Q 8 7
♡ J 7 6 4
◇ A 8
♣ A Q 5

South	West	North	East
1NT (15-17)	Pass	2♣	Pass
2♡	Pass	3♣	Pass
3♠	Pass	4♠	All Pass

You try the ◇ Q from dummy on West's lead and it holds the trick.

After Stayman the auction rather petered out. 3♠ agreed spades (North's Stayman enquiry promising one four-card major), so perhaps North might have tried a cue-bid next, or 4♣?

So it goes, another slam missed, but never mind, it might be your lucky day – the slam might fall foul of bad breaks. Make sure that those breaks do not take care of your game too!

A

Dealer: South   Love All

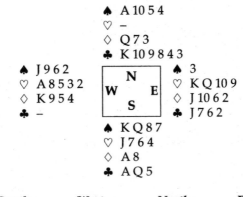

	♠ A 10 5 4	
	♡ –	
	◇ Q 7 3	
	♣ K 10 9 8 4 3	

♠ J 9 6 2		♠ 3
♡ A 8 5 3 2	**W N E S**	♡ K Q 10 9
◇ K 9 5 4		◇ J 10 6 2
♣ –		♣ J 7 6 2

	♠ K Q 8 7	
	♡ J 7 6 4	
	◇ A 8	
	♣ A Q 5	

South	West	North	East
1NT (15-17)	Pass	2♣	Pass
2♡	Pass	3♣	Pass
3♠	Pass	4♠	All Pass

You try the ◇Q from dummy on West's lead of the ◇4 and it wins.

Plenty of tricks – just two problems – bad club and spade breaks. If you start by cashing the ♠KQ then, on the layout above, you cannot cope. It is best to combine your chances by leaving open the option of ruffing two or even three hearts in dummy.

   Cash the ♠A.

(1) If both opponents follow, cash the ♣A:
–   If all follow then continue with trumps. A 3-2 break is easy, but if trumps are 4-1 you must leave one out and switch to clubs – the defender can take his outstanding trump when he wants, you always have another trump in dummy;
–   If West ruffs the ♣A, then ruff the heart return, cash the ♠K and ruff another heart. Cross to hand with the ◇A and draw the last trump. That makes three top spades, two ruffs and two diamonds; you still have two club tricks and a trump to come. Ten tricks.

(2) Someone shows out on the ♠A. Play to ruff three hearts – you need clubs to be 3-1. Cash the ♣A and ruff a heart, diamond to the ace, ruff a heart, diamond ruff, heart ruff, and the ♠KQ to come. Again, ten tricks.

Q

Dealer: North   Love All

```
              ♠ 10 9 3
              ♡ K 4
              ◇ Q J 9 7 4
              ♣ A K 5
                        ♠ A K 7 2
              N         ♡ A Q 9 5
Lead = ◇5   W   E       ◇ 10
              S         ♣ 9 7 3 2
```

South	West	North	East
		1◇	Double
1♠	Pass	2♠	Pass
3◇	Pass	4♠	All Pass

Declarer wins the ◇K in hand and then leads a trump to the ten –
over to you.

Partner has found a clever lead, hitting your singleton, but a heart
would have been more successful, wrapping up the defence's four
tricks straight away. As it is, with partner unlikely to have an entry, it
could be rather difficult to take your four tricks.

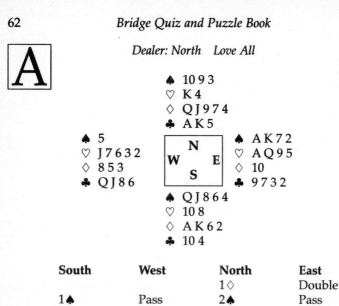

A

Dealer: North   Love All

♠ 10 9 3
♡ K 4
◇ Q J 9 7 4
♣ A K 5

♠ 5   ♠ A K 7 2
♡ J 7 6 3 2   ♡ A Q 9 5
◇ 8 5 3   ◇ 10
♣ Q J 8 6   ♣ 9 7 3 2

♠ Q J 8 6 4
♡ 10 8
◇ A K 6 2
♣ 10 4

South	West	North	East
		1◇	Double
1♠	Pass	2♠	Pass
3◇	Pass	4♠	All Pass

Declarer wins your partner's diamond lead in hand with the ◇ K and then leads a trump to the ten.

If you just play passively, declarer will have ten tricks – five diamonds, two clubs and three spades. So what can you do about it? You have to try and make an entry for partner so he can give you a ruff. Your only chance for this is if he has the ♡ J.

So, duck the first trump (best technique) and win the second. Now comes the ♡ Q. Ducking obviously does declarer no good at all, so he wins in dummy and plays another trump. But you win and underlead your ♡ A to give partner the lead with the ♡ J. You collect your fourth trick the hard way when he finally leads a diamond for you to ruff.

With a hand as well placed as this, do not always sit back and wait for the defence to prevail; sometimes your 'obvious' defensive tricks will disappear.

Q

Dealer: East   North-South Game

```
                  ♠ 6 4 3
                  ♡ K 8
                  ◊ Q J 7 5
                  ♣ K Q 4 2
                      N
Lead = ♡10    W         E
                      S
                  ♠ K J 9 8 5 2
                  ♡ 6
                  ◊ A K 3
                  ♣ A 10 8
```

South	West	North	East
			1♡[1]
1♠	4♡	Double[2]	Pass
4♠	All Pass		

[1] five-card major
[2] two-way – showing mixed values and some spade support

West's ♡10 lead goes to the king and ace. East switches to the ◊9.

With such poor spades North was loath to bid 4♠ over 4♡, especially with all his intermediate honours. But he did want to do something and thus passed the buck to you. Pass was tempting, but with the adverse vulnerability you would need four off to beat your own 4♠. A slam try was another option with a hand at least twice as good as an average overcall, but eventually you decided to settle for a simple game bonus.

Once dummy hit you knew you had made the right decision – 5♠ looks uncomfortable! Basking in the glory of your great judgement, you had better make sure you make 4♠.

A

Dealer: East   North-South Game

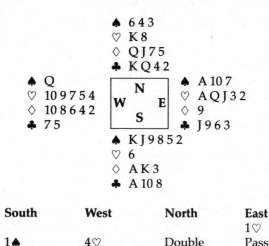

♠ 6 4 3
♡ K 8
◇ Q J 7 5
♣ K Q 4 2

♠ Q
♡ 10 9 7 5 4
◇ 10 8 6 4 2
♣ 7 5

♠ A 10 7
♡ A Q J 3 2
◇ 9
♣ J 9 6 3

♠ K J 9 8 5 2
♡ 6
◇ A K 3
♣ A 10 8

South	West	North	East
			1♡
1♠	4♡	Double	Pass
4♠	All Pass		

West's ♡10 lead goes to the king and ace. East switches to the ◇9.

There are two problems: a bad trump break, and a diamond singleton with East. How will you cope with these problems?

The opponents have 14 points between them, so a void spade in the weak hand is not an impossibility. East must hold the ♠A for with just 10 points he would not have opened the bidding. To manage a 4-0 trump break it looks right to finesse the ♠J, but you are happy to lose two trump tricks, so you do not need to take such a risk.

Let the diamond run to table and play a spade to the king. When this drops the queen, the contract is easy, but suppose West discards on the king. Now go back to dummy with the ♣Q and lead another spade. East wins and plays a heart, but you ruff in hand, cross to the ♣K and lead a third trump. Whether East wins this or not, his top trump is his last trick.

West's 4♡ was a very good bid. It is not that dangerous at favourable vulnerability, and it certainly made things difficult for partner. 4♡ is actually quite likely to make, requiring very accurate defence to defeat it – a trump lead on which North must withhold his king.

Dealer: South   East-West Game   Teams

♠ Q 10 4 2
♡ A 4
◇ A K
♣ J 10 9 6 4

Lead = ♣7

```
        N
    W       E
        S
```

♠ 9
♡ 9 6 3
◇ Q 7 6 5 3
♣ A K 5 2

South	West	North	East
1♠	Pass	2♣	Pass
2♠	Pass	4♠	All Pass

You win your ♣K and declarer follows with the queen.

Who has what? Was the lead a singleton, doubleton or MUD from three cards?

What do you do?

Dealer: South   East-West Game   Teams

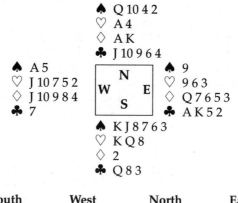

♠ Q 10 4 2
♡ A 4
♢ A K
♣ J 10 9 6 4

♠ A 5
♡ J 10 7 5 2
♢ J 10 9 8 4
♣ 7

♠ 9
♡ 9 6 3
♢ Q 7 6 5 3
♣ A K 5 2

♠ K J 8 7 6 3
♡ K Q 8
♢ 2
♣ Q 8 3

South	West	North	East
1♠	Pass	2♣	Pass
2♠	Pass	4♠	All Pass

Partner leads the ♣7 which you win with your ♣K and declarer follows with the queen.

As suggested, the important question is how many clubs has partner?

If partner has three cards declarer is likely to make his contract – he may lose a heart and a trump, but that is surely all. Note that partner is unlikely to lead dummy's suit without a good reason, and three small cards is certainly not a good reason.

If partner has two clubs, it is less clear – you have two clubs, possibly a heart and possibly a trump. You will need a trump trick and so can afford to cash the second club and then lead a heart to establish a trick in that suit.

If partner has one club, then you need to cash both clubs, give partner a ruff, and then hope for a trump trick.

From the above analysis it is clear that cashing a second club is the best line. It doesn't matter if South can ruff, for he was going to make his contract anyway! Remember overtricks are not so important in Teams.

On this hand you take the first two clubs and give partner a ruff, with the ♠A still to come.

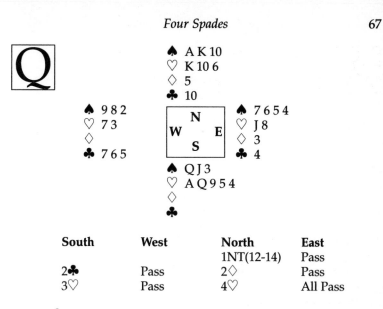

South	West	North	East
		1NT(12-14)	Pass
2♣	Pass	2◇	Pass
3♡	Pass	4♡	All Pass

Lead = ♣K

Not playing transfers, South's sequence (using Stayman) showed an invitation to game with five or more hearts.

A teacher was taking a class of beginners and was mystified when she arrived at this table to discover that South was declaring 4♡, but had lost the first five tricks. She was not sure that they could have bid correctly and would like to have checked, but the tricks taken had been piled together. Perhaps you could help her?

The students always play their lowest card first, unless they have a winner or they have a card ranking one higher than the card played by RHO – i.e. if the ◇Q is played, next hand will play the ◇K if he has it, but if the ◇J is led, next hand will not play the ◇K, only the ◇Q if he has it. They would never overtake partner's winner.

The lead of the king may be from ace-king or king-queen.

The only part of the play that the students could remember was that West had won the first trick, East the second, then West, then East, then West – they had thought it funny at the time!

All that remains is to tell you that the beginners' bidding was perfectly reasonable. Can you tell the teacher the exact layout of the hands? And tell the students which game contract would have made.

```
                    ♠ A K 10
                    ♡ K 10 6
                    ◇ K 10 5 4
                    ♣ 10 9 8
      ♠ 9 8 2        ┌─────────┐        ♠ 7 6 5 4
      ♡ 7 3 2        │    N    │        ♡ J 8
      ◇ Q 9        W │         │ E       ◇ A J 3 2
      ♣ A K 7 6 5     │    S    │        ♣ 4 3 2
                    └─────────┘
                    ♠ Q J 3
                    ♡ A Q 9 5 4
                    ◇ 8 7 6
                    ♣ Q J
```

West wins the first trick with the ♣K. If he had ♣KQ, where has the queen gone? The ace, which has been played, must have won the second round of the suit – West could not have had the queen. Knowing that West started with the ♣AK allows you to fill in the club suit. East must have 432 because he still has the ♣4 left and would have played up the line. That leaves just the eight and nine left below the ten (West holds 765), and they must belong to North so that he could play up the line, which leaves South with QJ.

You were told that West won three tricks, two club tricks and ? There is a trump missing from the diagram and East could not have played one – he has no void – so West's third trick must have been a diamond ruff (with the ♡2).

Now you have the picture: East must have won two diamond tricks. But looking at the small cards left there must have been some big diamonds played on the first two rounds. North has 10 points and to raise to game he would need 14, or a good 13 (he has three tens already so he might have a good 13).

Try KJxx to give him a 14-count. To get North to play his ◇K West must have played the ◇Q, but that would establish a trick for North – so that is no good. Try K10xx. Yes, now you are getting there: to get North to play his two honours West must hold the cards immediately beneath them – ◇Q9 doubleton.

The small cards are easily filled in: East's must be lower than the three, i.e. the two! North's must be lower than the five (but not the three or two), i.e. the four. Which leaves the 876 for South.

The answer to the second question is that on this occasion, because of the combined club holdings, 3NT would have made easily.

CHAPTER 4

Weak Two

More and more pre-emptive tools are being introduced into bridge at all levels. The most common addition is the proliferation of weak two bids. This type of bid shows a six-card suit and 6-9 points.

This chapter contains hands where a weak two has been used. The hands show how disruptive the bids can be, but also show the negative sides of the bids, which make declarer-play a little easier.

Q

Dealer: East   Game All

```
              ♠ 3
              ♡ J 10 7
              ◇ A Q 8 6 4
              ♣ Q 10 7 2
                 ┌─────────┐
                 │    N    │
Lead = ♠A        │  W   E  │
                 │    S    │
                 └─────────┘
              ♠ J 10
              ♡ A K Q 9 8 6 2
              ◇ 9 7
              ♣ A 3
```

South	West	North	East
			2♠ (weak)
4♡	4♠	5♡	All Pass

West leads the ♠A followed by the ♠2.

Prospects do not look too bad. It looks like a good guess in clubs will mean you don't need the diamond finesse.

What line do you take for eleven tricks?

A

Dealer: East   Game All

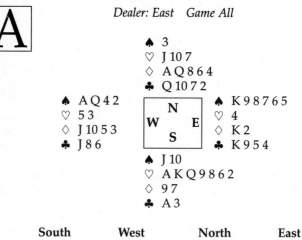

♠ 3
♡ J 10 7
◇ A Q 8 6 4
♣ Q 10 7 2

♠ A Q 4 2
♡ 5 3
◇ J 10 5 3
♣ J 8 6

♠ K 9 8 7 6 5
♡ 4
◇ K 2
♣ K 9 5 4

♠ J 10
♡ A K Q 9 8 6 2
◇ 9 7
♣ A 3

South	West	North	East
			2♠ (weak)
4♡	4♠	5♡	All Pass

West leads the ♠A followed by the ♠2.

A good guess in clubs will mean you don't need the diamond finesse, but a good guess in clubs is just 50%. At the table, the declarer disagreed. He ruffed the second heart, drew trumps, cashed the ♣A and played a club to the queen. East won and exited with a spade. Declarer ruffed and confidently finessed in diamonds – one down. He expected East to have better spades for his weak two and thus only one minor-suit king.

There are two ways to play the contract: one is to get rid of the diamond loser as above, but the other is to get rid of the club loser – a much better line.

Play a small diamond from dummy at trick two. Win the club return with the ace, play a diamond to the ace and ruff a diamond high, play a trump to the ♡10 and ruff another diamond high. A trump to the ♡J (drawing the last trump) enables you to cash dummy's established diamond, throwing your losing club.

Of course on this layout things are made slightly easier when the king falls beneath the ace.

You do need trumps to split 2-1 and diamonds 4-2, but the odds are in your favour, so this line is certainly best.

Dealer: South   Game All

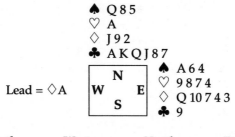

Q

♠ Q 8 5
♡ A
♢ J 9 2
♣ A K Q J 8 7

Lead = ♢ A

```
        N        ♠ A 6 4
  W         E    ♡ 9 8 7 4
        S        ♢ Q 10 7 4 3
                 ♣ 9
```

South	**West**	**North**	**East**
2♠ (weak)	Double	4♠	All Pass

Your partner makes a take-out double of South's weak two, but North shuts out any thoughts that you had of entering the auction.

Any ideas?

Dealer: South   Game All

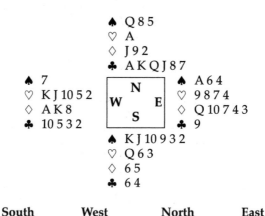

	South	**West**	**North**	**East**
	2♠ (weak)	Double	4♠	All Pass

West leads the ◇ A.

An odd hand. Only 17 points, but you can make 4♡ (even 5♡ on a non-club lead). The opponents have bid well and might even make their contract. A double game swing would look ugly on the score-card.

It is important for partner to switch to a club. A small discouraging diamond might do the trick, but why should he think there is any urgency to the switch? With the clubs on table partner might try to cash a second diamond before they run away. (The low diamond might be seen to deny the ◇Q rather than suggesting an urgent switch.) Furthermore, partner might see a heart as the best switch, knocking out declarer's entry and making the play more awkward for him. Do not let partner think of any alternatives! You know the club position and should try to get the message across to partner.

The ◇Q should do the trick – obviously a glaring signal with the ◇J on the table. Partner will probably expect you to have a void club and will be mystified when he finds the switch and you follow suit. But you win the first round of trumps and send a diamond back to partner who will give you the setting trick with a club ruff. Not +620, but +100 will have to do.

Dealer: South   East-West Game

```
                    ♠ 10 7 6 5
                    ♡ A 4
                    ♦ A 7
                    ♣ A K 9 5 3
                         N
   Lead = ♠A      W         E
                         S
                    ♠ J 8
                    ♡ K Q 9 8 5 3
                    ♦ J 9 8
                    ♣ 8 2
```

South	West	North	East
2♡ (weak)	Double	4♡	All Pass

West leads the ♠A, ♠K and switches to the ♡2.

A simple auction has brought you to a reasonable contract, although 3NT may have been easier, especially as any chance of getting a ruff in dummy has disappeared.

How should you proceed?

A

Dealer: South   East-West Game

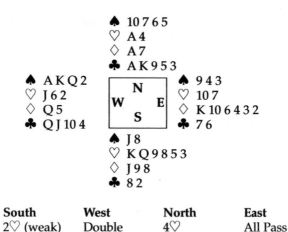

♠ 10 7 6 5
♡ A 4
◇ A 7
♣ A K 9 5 3

♠ A K Q 2
♡ J 6 2
◇ Q 5
♣ Q J 10 4

♠ 9 4 3
♡ 10 7
◇ K 10 6 4 3 2
♣ 7 6

♠ J 8
♡ K Q 9 8 5 3
◇ J 9 8
♣ 8 2

South	**West**	**North**	**East**
2♡ (weak)	Double	4♡	All Pass

West leads the ♠A, ♠K and switches to the ♡2.

There are two chances, the most likely being to establish the club suit and for that you have to use dummy's entries wisely. Let the trump come round to hand, play a club to the ♣A and ruff a spade back to hand. There is just a chance that the player who started with three spades holds the ♠Q, but that is not to be. The main chance is to cash the ♣K, ruff a club, play a trump to the ace and ruff another club. Now draw the last trump and cross to dummy's ◇A to enjoy the established club.

West might have tried a diamond switch but from his holding it was uninviting and would have given declarer his tenth trick in diamonds.

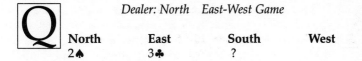

Q   *Dealer: North   East-West Game*

North	East	South	West
2♠	3♣	?	

Your partner has opened a weak two at favourable vulnerability (showing six cards and 4-8 points), and right-hand opponent overcalls naturally in clubs.

What do you bid with the following?

(A)   ♠ 5
        ♡ K Q 4 2
        ◇ K Q 5 4 3
        ♣ K Q 6

(B)   ♠ 8 3 2
        ♡ 5 2
        ◇ A Q 5 4 3
        ♣ 7 6 3

(C)   ♠ K 5 4 2
        ♡ 5 2
        ◇ A 6 5 4 3 2
        ♣ 8

(D)   ♠ K 5 4 2
        ♡ 5 2
        ◇ A K 5 4 3 2
        ♣ 8

(E)   ♠ 2
        ♡ K 8 6
        ◇ A K Q 5 4 3
        ♣ K Q 6

(A) Pass. A lovely hand, but nowhere to go. Double is speculative – you may have four tricks in your own hand, but why should partner have one? Remember this is favourable vulnerability. Partner might simply hold ♠KJ10xxx and there will be no entries to his hand. The lack of intermediates is something to watch. If you broadcast your hand and your strength by doubling you will probably make 3♣ easier, and will leave yourself open to endplays. Wait and hope the opposition bid on, at which point you will be ready! As for 3NT, where are the tricks going to come from? With no source of tricks 3NT will definitely be a struggle (c.f. hand E).

(B) 3♠. Little strength, but a nine-card fit. Continue the obstruction, trying to keep them out of their heart fit. This might seem like overbidding, but the opponents should be scoring game (they have between 26 and 30 points) so that 3♠ doubled three down would be a good sacrifice: –500 against –620 for 4♡. They might even make slam!

(C) 4♠. Again, little strength, but this time a ten-card fit. Make things as difficult as possible. They may settle for 300 or 500, rather than an easy 620 or 650 in the, as yet, undiscovered heart fit (or even 600 in 5♣). Note, partner need only hold ♠Axxxxx and you should make seven tricks plus any ruffs there are going. Of course if he holds a singleton diamond he may well make 4♠!

(D) 4♢. Similar to the last hand, but with extra strength in a side-suit. This bid, though natural, does promise good support for the suit opened – a *fit bid*. Although it gives LHO the chance to bid 4♡, the extra information the bid gives partner is invaluable, making it easier for him to make a decision at the five level. With this hand there is a much greater chance that 4♠ will make so the decision on the next round may be very important.

(E) 3NT. A good source of tricks, and a good club stop – definitely worth a risk. Two reasons: (i) it might make! (ii) they might not double and 3♣ might make, so that 3NT – 2 for –100 will compare favourably with –110 for 3♣. The one thing against 3NT is that a heart lead might make things awkward. Still, if the diamonds come in, it will never be too bad.

Dealer: East   Love All

♠ Q J 6 4 3
♡ A J 6
◇ Q 8
♣ 8 4 3

Lead = ♡3

```
      N
  W       E
      S
```

♠ A K 10
♡ K 8 5
◇ K 6 4 3 2
♣ A 9

South	West	North	East
			2♡ (weak)
2NT (16-19)	Pass	3♡[1]	Pass
3♠[1]	Pass	3NT	Pass
4♣[2]	Pass	4♠	All Pass

[1] transfer to spades   [2] cue-bid

There are nine easy tricks, and plenty of chances for a tenth, but there are a number of obvious dangers, not least, heart ruffs. How do you play?

A

Dealer: East Love All

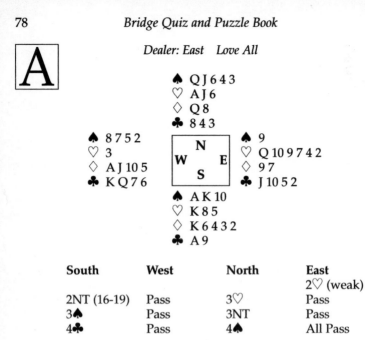

♠ Q J 6 4 3
♡ A J 6
◇ Q 8
♣ 8 4 3

♠ 8 7 5 2
♡ 3
◇ A J 10 5
♣ K Q 7 6

W N E S

♠ 9
♡ Q 10 9 7 4 2
◇ 9 7
♣ J 10 5 2

♠ A K 10
♡ K 8 5
◇ K 6 4 3 2
♣ A 9

South	West	North	East
			2♡ (weak)
2NT (16-19)	Pass	3♡	Pass
3♠	Pass	3NT	Pass
4♣	Pass	4♠	All Pass

West led the ♡3.

Dummy reversal? Establishing diamonds? Ruffing a club? You have plenty of options for the tenth trick. The latter is flawed, for if you give up a club West might get two heart ruffs (if East holds the ◇A). The other options involve ruffing two or three diamonds, so you should certainly play on that suit first.

Win the ♡K in hand and play a diamond to the queen. If this holds, continue in diamonds. You can cope with whatever West does now. A non-diamond switch means you can negotiate a club ruff safely. If he switches to a diamond you ruff high, then play the ♠A, and a heart towards dummy. West does best to discard, but you win the ♡A, cross to the ♠K, ruff a fourth diamond and cross back to the ♣A. Finally the last diamond completes your plan. West ruffs but you overruff and still have the ♠10 to come.

If East had taken the second trick with the ◇A he has no winning options – giving his partner a heart ruff makes things easier for declarer and if he does not give him a ruff then declarer can simply play to ruff a club!

♠ 10
                              ♡ K 6 4 2
                              ◇ K J 7
                              ♣ A K 8 3 2
          ♠ K Q J 9 3 2   ┌─────────┐
          ♡ 7 3   │   N   │
          ◇ 10 9 6 4   │ W   E │
          ♣ 7   │   S   │
                           └─────────┘

South	West	North	East
	2♠ (weak)	Double	Pass
3NT	All Pass		

You lead the ♠K, which is allowed to hold, partner playing the ♠4
and declarer the ♠5.

For a change you have a respectable suit, and thus started the
defence quite confidently. What next?

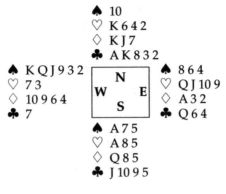

South	West	North	East
	2♠ (weak)	Double	Pass
3NT	All Pass		

You lead the ♠K, which holds, partner playing the ♠4 and declarer the ♠5.

The problem with playing conventions is that you cannot always make the bid you want to! South would have preferred to bid 2NT, but that would have been unnatural (Lebensohl) so he decided to go straight to game.

You should not be swayed from your suit right away because partner's first card should show *count*. The ♠4 is the smallest card he can hold so he must have an odd number. Declarer will have to hold up a second round.

When you cash the ♠Q partner will be able to give you a message. He will try to suggest you switch to his best suit. To do this he will play his highest spade to suggest the highest suit in dummy (hearts) and his lowest spade to suggest a lower suit, in this instance diamonds, clubs being excluded because of dummy's strength there.

So when partner plays the ♠8 on your ♠Q you can confidently switch to hearts. Now declarer, who still has to lose the lead twice, cannot stop East establishing two heart tricks.

Even without the signal you might guess the right switch, but the key to successful defence is a good dialogue between the two players.

Dealer: East   East-West Game

         ♠ 7 4 3
         ♡ A Q 5 2
         ◇ K 5 3
         ♣ Q J 7

Lead = ♠6

	N	
W		**E**
	S	

         ♠ 9
         ♡ 10 8 7
         ◇ A 8 2
         ♣ A K 9 6 5 3

South	**West**	**North**	**East**
			2♠ (weak)
3♣	Pass	3♠[1]	Double
4♣	Pass	5♣	All Pass

[1] asking for a spade stop

East wins trick one with the ♠J and then plays the ♠A. You ruff and draw trumps in two rounds.

North has a reasonable hand, but at this vulnerability South did not promise anything special for his overcall. It is lucky that 5♣ has some play.

    What do you make of East's defence? Has it affected your thoughts on the hand?

A

Dealer: East   East-West Game

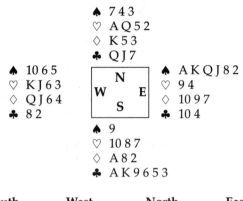

	♠ 7 4 3	
	♡ A Q 5 2	
	◇ K 5 3	
	♣ Q J 7	

♠ 10 6 5		♠ A K Q J 8 2
♡ K J 6 3	N	♡ 9 4
◇ Q J 6 4	W E	◇ 10 9 7
♣ 8 2	S	♣ 10 4

	♠ 9	
	♡ 10 8 7	
	◇ A 8 2	
	♣ A K 9 6 5 3	

South	West	North	East
			2♠ (weak)
3♣	Pass	3♠	Double
4♣	Pass	5♣	All Pass

East wins trick one with the ♠J and then plays the ♠A. You ruff and draw trumps in two rounds.

East's defence was very silly because he has revealed his whole hand. Can he have anything more than ♠AKQJxx? Many would open this 1♠ anyway, but with as little as a jack outside he would probably have opened at the one level.

If you can make three heart tricks that will take your total to eleven (with six clubs and two diamonds). Obviously with the finesse right a 3-3 break would make it easy, but what about 4-2 breaks?

Any endplay will fail because of a lack of communication so you must concentrate on the heart suit. Because of the holes in the suit, you need a special play called an intra-finesse.

After drawing trumps lead a heart from dummy (yes, away from the ♡AQ), and finesse East for the ♡9 by inserting the ♡8. West wins the ♡J. Win his diamond return and lead the ♡10, pinning East's ♡9. Whether West covers or not you have established the suit.

Notice that had the ♡8 lost to the ♡9 you would later run the ten (no doubt covered by the jack) and then run the seven. You would still succeed as long as East held the ♡6.

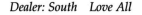

Dealer: South   Love All

Q

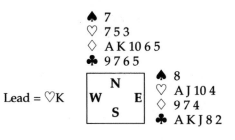

```
              ♠ 7
              ♡ 7 5 3
              ◇ A K 10 6 5
              ♣ 9 7 6 5
                              ♠ 8
          N                   ♡ A J 10 4
Lead = ♡K    W     E          ◇ 9 7 4
          S                   ♣ A K J 8 2
```

South	**West**	**North**	**East**
2♠ (weak)	Pass	Pass	Double[1]
All Pass			

[1] take-out

Defending against low-level doubled contracts requires great accuracy, especially when you might have a game on.

You are not sure whether you have a heart fit, let alone whether 4♡ makes, but you would like to get 2♠ down three for reassurance.

What plan do you have?

A

Dealer: South   Love All

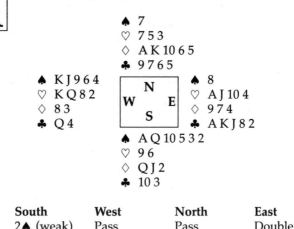

♠ 7
♡ 7 5 3
◇ A K 10 6 5
♣ 9 7 6 5

♠ K J 9 6 4
♡ K Q 8 2
◇ 8 3
♣ Q 4

♠ 8
♡ A J 10 4
◇ 9 7 4
♣ A K J 8 2

♠ A Q 10 5 3 2
♡ 9 6
◇ Q J 2
♣ 10 3

South	West	North	East
2♠ (weak)	Pass	Pass	Double
All Pass			

West leads the ♡K.

A look at dummy suggests that you probably have the values for a game, so you should be looking to get 2♠ three down.

Your plan should focus on trying to stop partner being endplayed in trumps at the end of the hand. To this end: (1) avoid reducing declarer's trumps; (2) play a trump through declarer early; (3) play a suit through declarer in which both he and partner are void.

To achieve (1) you will need count in hearts so play the ♡10 to show an even number (not the ♡J which might simply promise the ten). For the rest of the plan you need to obtain the lead as often as possible.

After the ♡K partner continues with his lowest heart (showing three remaining). Win the ♡A and play a trump. Declarer plays the ♠A, cashes the ◇A and ◇K, ruffs a heart and exits with a club. Win this and give partner a diamond ruff. Then follow two more rounds of clubs. Partner overruffs declarer's forced ruff. Now the coup de grace as partner plays his last heart to endplay declarer. You make 2♠!! (or in this case take 2♠ three down!).

What difference would playing a third heart straight away make? Try it for yourself, but best declarer play will have your partner endplayed instead – all a question of timing.

Q

♠ 10 5 3
♡ K Q 8 6
♢ A Q 4
♣ Q 8 2

Lead = ♠6

```
      N
  W       E
      S
```

♠ A 8
♡ 9 3
♢ K J 10 7 6
♣ K 7 5 3

South	West	North	East
	2♠ (weak)	Double	Pass
3NT	All Pass		

West's ♠6 lead goes to East's king.

Oh dear! This does not look too good. The pre-emptive bid has done its job and propelled you into a rather awkward contract. Have you any chances?

A

Dealer: West   Game All

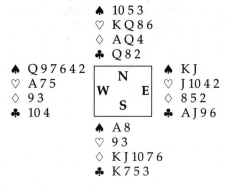

♠ 10 5 3
♡ K Q 8 6
◇ A Q 4
♣ Q 8 2

♠ Q 9 7 6 4 2   ♠ K J
♡ A 7 5   ♡ J 10 4 2
◇ 9 3   ◇ 8 5 2
♣ 10 4   ♣ A J 9 6

♠ A 8
♡ 9 3
◇ K J 10 7 6
♣ K 7 5 3

South	West	North	East
	2♠ (weak)	Double	Pass
3NT	All Pass		

West's ♠6 lead goes to East's king.

You do indeed have little chance. West has to have one of the outstanding aces, especially at this vulnerability, so the obvious hold-up will be useless. Your only chance is for a blockage in the spade suit, playing East for two honours. So you have to take the ♠A right away.

Remember that this is not a simple matter of stopping your opponents running their spade suit, you do need nine tricks yourself.

If you play on clubs and West has that ace, you need it to be doubleton – not good odds.

If you play on hearts and West has that ace you can play up to the king, and then up to the queen later. This should work most of the time and so, going for the best odds, you assume that West has the ♡A.

Win the ♠A and play a heart. West ducks and you win the king. A diamond to the ten is followed by another heart. West wins this and plays a spade to East's jack. East has no way of putting West back in and so you are safe to establish a ninth trick in clubs.

If West ducks the second heart, your queen wins and you must play a small heart from dummy, cutting the defenders' communications otherwise East can cash the ♠J and then play a heart to West's ace.

In the grid below are seated four characters playing bridge. The four had been playing another game, but had set aside (in the grid) that equipment to join your table.

Where is the game taking place, who is the declarer, what was the lead, and what was the outcome of the hand?

In fact, there is a whole story hidden below – kibitzers, comments, forgotten conventions, even the declarer's lucky companion. See how much you can find.

The secrets are not hidden in straight lines but bend back and forth, adjacent letters always touching in the grid. Their shapes are often relevant.

Clues: the players are seated as and where you would expect them; another book is required to get to the bottom of this puzzle.

V	E	E	T	A	D	T	P	Q	H	E	S	H	A	D	E	F	I	V	E
E	N	V	W	P	E	O	B	A	C	E	R	I	M	S	K	R	U	O	C
S	F	I	O	S	S	P	D	E	X	C	A	T	R	I	C	T	I	E	R
F	L	O	W	E	R	K	Y	C	I	L	B	N	C	R	R	U	O	F	S
T	S	U	I	O	L	P	G	I	E	N	O	R	A	A	S	O	L	D	I
U	J	Z	F	D	D	A	E	L	E	H	F	U	T	D	N	A	S	R	E
Q	L	M	A	R	N	V	E	A	R	T	N	O	W	I	P	Z	C	V	I
I	E	Q	R	T	P	S	H	M	N	V	X	V	A	G	N	I	K	L	K
R	H	U	D	I	Y	T	E	R	O	Q	U	E	B	O	C	L	E	A	D
H	T	E	M	F	L	R	A	C	R	O	U	T	N	F	H	P	O	E	M
E	H	E	O	L	H	A	P	R	G	D	N	C	I	E	W	V	J	L	T
A	T	N	F	O	F	E	N	W	O	N	D	E	D	A	R	T	S	K	R
D	I	W	F	C	V	X	K	D	N	A	L	R	X	O	P	W	A	M	D
S	D	Q	A	V	U	E	J	D	I	H	W	A	B	C	D	F	G	E	X
E	T	L	U	B	H	C	H	G	T	W	X	E	O	L	D	I	L	D	I
A	I	I	T	A	N	U	G	K	E	R	A	L	P	O	W	E	O	C	E
Z	E	C	N	R	I	T	A	M	V	W	B	Q	R	S	C	R	S	W	R
N	O	S	I	J	P	I	E	R	T	I	B	C	E	A	M	I	N	G	O
U	C	S	R	E	N	O	L	O	O	D	L	C	I	L	H	O	G	S	S
D	H	E	P	N	P	T	O	W	K	C	A	U	V	F	E	G	D	E	H

The four players, of course, were the King and Queen of Hearts, the White Rabbit and Alice (playing in 4NT). The game was being played on the croquet ground in Wonderland (middle of grid). The players had placed the mallets (flamingos) and balls (hedgehogs) with a couple of hoops (soldiers) in the bottom right-hand corner of the grid.

Alice made (top right) five courtiers (diamonds), four soldiers (clubs) and won the lead (with the ♡A, the only card to overtake the ♡K), therefore making 4NT. Not the right contract because the Rabbit had forgotten Blackwood (beneath him), but at least it was made.

The Queen had enough gardeners (spades) to defeat the contract easily, but her partner never failed to lead himself ('I lead me!') if he had the chance. Angry at the King, she knew he would not understand, so the kibitzers had to suffer. 'Off with their heads! (middle left) she shouted, but by that time Alice had carefully placed the threesome in a flowerpot (top left). Getting angrier still, the Queen turned her wrath on Alice's friend, the Cheshire Cat (who had advised her from above during the play). She demanded that the cat lose its head, but this caused considerable consternation for the cat had no body to lose its head from. After much arguing Alice said that the only person who could resolve the problem was the Duchess. She, of course, was in prison (bottom left) and so the Queen sent the executioner to get her out.

V	E	E	T	A	D	T			H	E	S	H	A	D	E	F	I	V	E
E	N	V	W	P	E	O			C	E	R	I	M	S	K	R	U	O	C
S	F	I	O	S	S	P		E		C	A	T	R	I	C	T	I	E	R
F	L	O	W	E	R			C	I			N		R	U	O	F	S	
							I		N		R		S	O	L	D	I		
				D	A	E	L	E	H	F	U		D	N	A	S	R	E	
						A		T	N	O	W	I							
I	E	Q			S					G	N	I	K						
R	H	U			T	R	O	Q	U	E		O		L	E	A	D		
H	T	E		F		R		C	R	O	U	T		F	H			E	M
E	H	E	O		H	A			G	D	N		E						
A	T	N	F		E	W	O	N	D	E		A	R	T	S				
D	I	W	F		X	D	N	A	L	R									
S				E		I	H	W											
			C		T			L	D	I	L	D	I						
			U		E	R	A		O		E	O		E					
			T			B		S		R	S		R						
N	O	S	I		I	T	I	B		A	M	I	N	G	O				
U	C	S	R	E	N	O		O	O	D	L	L	H	O	G	S	S		
D	H	E	P			W	K	C	A		F	E	G	D	E	H			

CHAPTER 5
Wrong Contract

It happens all too often – you get lost in the auction and find yourself in the wrong contract. Rather than concentrating hard on the play, you find yourself dwelling on partner's bad bidding. Whatever contract you finish in, you must put all your efforts into making it.

This chapter does not deal with the bidding calamities that leave you in completely hopeless contracts, but with those times when you see dummy and your first thought is 'Such and such looks a better contract.' You must then make every effort to rescue the situation and make your contract better.

Q

Dealer: South   Love All

```
            ♠ K J 9
            ♡ 2
            ◇ J 4 3 2
            ♣ A J 7 6 4
                         ♠ A 5
              N          ♡ A 10 8 5 4
Lead = ♠3   W   E        ◇ K 9 8
              S          ♣ K 9 2
```

South	West	North	East
1♠	Pass	2♣	Pass
2♡	Pass	3♠	All Pass

North might have done better simply to raise 1♠ to 2♠; instead he has managed to put his side's partscore in jeopardy. Can you punish him for his extravagance?

Partner leads the ♠3 which you win and return another trump, won in dummy. Next comes dummy's singleton heart. What is your plan?

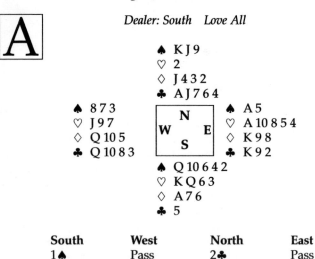

A

Dealer: South   Love All

♠ K J 9
♡ 2
◇ J 4 3 2
♣ A J 7 6 4

♠ 8 7 3
♡ J 9 7
◇ Q 10 5
♣ Q 10 8 3

♠ A 5
♡ A 10 8 5 4
◇ K 9 8
♣ K 9 2

♠ Q 10 6 4 2
♡ K Q 6 3
◇ A 7 6
♣ 5

South	West	North	East
1♠	Pass	2♣	Pass
2♡	Pass	3♠	All Pass

Partner leads the ♠3 which you win and return another trump, won in dummy. Next comes dummy's singleton heart.

Remember that there is only one trump on table and South has already shown four hearts, so you should not be thinking that this is your only chance to win a heart trick. If you jump in with the ace you are likely to establish tricks for declarer and in any event you cannot stop his ruff. If South has any two honours you give away a trick: with KQxx he will make two heart tricks and a ruff; similarly with KJxx (partner's queen will fall on the third round); and with QJxx he will be able to take a ruffing finesse, although he will still lose one more trick in the suit.

If you duck, all sorts of good things may happen – the possibilites are endless. It certainly pays dividends here. Declarer wins with the ♡Q and ruffs a heart, but he has nowhere to put his other two hearts, so has to lose two hearts, one spade, and two diamonds for one down.

If you rise with the ♡A declarer can win any return and is still able to ruff his fourth heart, taking him to nine tricks – two hearts, one ruff, four trumps and two minor-suit aces.

Q

Dealer: North   Love All

```
              ♠ 10 4
              ♡ 7 2
              ◇ A K Q J 6 4
              ♣ K 7 2
```

			N		
Lead = ♡K	**W**			**E**	
			S		

```
              ♠ A K Q 9
              ♡ 5
              ◇ 8 3
              ♣ Q J 9 8 5 3
```

South	West	North	East
		1◇	Pass
1♠	Pass	1NT (12-15)	Pass
3♣	Pass	3♠	Pass
4♣	Pass	4◇	Pass
4♡	Pass	4♠	All Pass

West led the ♡K and continued at trick two with the ♡Q.

What a mess! Sometimes one wheel comes off during the auction, but here all four seem to have disappeared. Luckily the Fates have left some bricks to rest the contract on.

With six clubs, four spades and the values for game opposite an opening bid, South should undoubtedly respond 2♣ in the first place but that was just the first wheel. 1NT misdescribed North's hand, next came 3♣ – accurate if late. North's 3♠ is indescribable, impossible to understand – his diamonds obviously were not good enough for him to bid a second time!! 4♣ at least told North that they were both missing heart values but when North finally rebid his diamonds his partner understandably took this for a cue-bid, replying with a cue-bid of his own, 4♡. They finally came to rest in 4♠.

Anyway, you are here now, and must put the aesthetics of the auction behind you. How can you make this contract?

A

Dealer: North   Love All

```
            ♠ 10 4
            ♡ 7 2
            ◇ A K Q J 6 4
            ♣ K 7 2
♠ 7 6 3          N          ♠ J 8 5 2
♡ K Q 10 9 8  W     E      ♡ A J 6 4 3
◇ 10 7 5          S          ◇ 9 2
♣ 10 6                       ♣ A 4
            ♠ A K Q 9
            ♡ 5
            ◇ 8 3
            ♣ Q J 9 8 5 3
```

South	West	North	East
		1◇	Pass
1♠	Pass	1NT (12-15)	Pass
3♣	Pass	3♠	Pass
4♣	Pass	4◇	Pass
4♡	Pass	4♠	All Pass

West led the ♡K followed by the ♡Q.

You cannot afford to lose trump control so ruffing the second trick is out of the question. You have to discard a club, leaving dummy to deal with a third heart. That makes two heart losers and the ♣A to come, so you cannot afford a trump loser.

Be sure to ruff the third heart with the ♠10 in order to unblock for the impending trump finesse. Yes, you have to take a trump finesse, and when that comes home you make just the eleven tricks!

As a defender I might well have had trouble accepting this one graciously, and yet we all have our strokes of luck. It is a matter of being able to calm yourself enough to play the hand. Here ducking the second heart and ruffing the third with the ♠10 are both essential plays, which could be easily missed if your eyes were not firmly centred on the ball. If you ruff the third heart small and lead the ♠10 which is ducked, you are stranded in dummy with no way back to hand.

Dealer: South   East-West Game

```
                  ♠ Q J 3
                  ♡ A J 3 2
                  ◇ A 6 4
                  ♣ A 9 6
                      N
Lead = ◇ K      W       E
                      S
                  ♠ A K 10 7 2
                  ♡ K Q 8 6
                  ◇ 10
                  ♣ 10 7 3
```

South	West	North	East
1♠[1]	3◇[2]	4◇[3]	Pass
4♡[4]	Pass	5♣[4]	Pass
5◇[4]	Pass	5♡[4]	Pass
5♠[5]	Pass	6♠[6]	All Pass

[1] five-card suit   [2] weak jump overcall   [3] strong with spade support
[4] cue-bids   [5] sign-off   [6] one for the road

East played the ◇J on his partner's opening lead of the ◇K.

Oh dear! 6♡ looks very easy – just one ruff takes the trick total to twelve. How did North-South get to 6♠?

I blame it on West! His 3◇ bid made life very difficult for North, and with an eight-card fit found in spades already, why go looking for another?

Can you rescue the situation?

A

Dealer: South   East-West Game

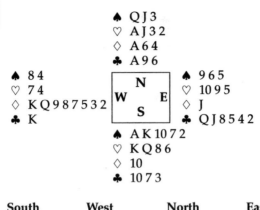

♠ Q J 3
♡ A J 3 2
◇ A 6 4
♣ A 9 6

♠ 8 4
♡ 7 4
◇ K Q 9 8 7 5 3 2
♣ K

♠ 9 6 5
♡ 10 9 5
◇ J
♣ Q J 8 5 4 2

♠ A K 10 7 2
♡ K Q 8 6
◇ 10
♣ 10 7 3

South	West	North	East
1♠	3◇	4◇	Pass
4♡	Pass	5♣	Pass
5◇	Pass	5♡	Pass
5♠	Pass	6♠	All Pass

West led the ◇K and East played the ◇J.

Desperate times call for desperate measures. The only possible chance is a partial elimination. You need West to hold two spades, just two hearts (if he had three hearts East would be able to ruff the third round), and two clubs, both of which need to be honours!!

OK, here goes! Win the ◇A and ruff a diamond, play a club to the ♣A, and ruff another diamond. Now the ♠A, ♠Q and two rounds of hearts. Finally play a club, but only now do you realise that even if you do get a ruff and discard you cannot draw East's last trump.

It is actually worse than it seems! You need West to hold doubletons in the majors as above but you also need him to have the singleton ♣K so that the ♣A acts as an entry later. This requires West to hold eight diamonds, just possible at this vulnerability.

So try again. Win the ◇A, cash two hearts (before East can discard them), and then ruff a diamond, ♠A, ♠Q, ruff another diamond, and finally play a low club. West does have to win and is forced to lead a diamond. You ruff in hand, cross to the ♣A and draw East's last trump.

That was pretty tough for a flat board!

Q

Dealer: West   Love All

```
            ♠ 10 3
            ♡ 7 6 4
            ◇ A Q 9 7 5 4
            ♣ 6 3
                    ┌─────────┐
                    │    N    │
Lead = ♠Q           │ W     E │
                    │    S    │
                    └─────────┘
            ♠ A 6 4
            ♡ A 9 5
            ◇ 8 6
            ♣ A Q J 10 5
```

South	West	North	East
	2♠ (weak)	Pass	Pass
2NT	Pass	3NT	All Pass

East overtakes the ♠Q lead with his ♠K. When you duck he continues with a second spade.

South's 2NT bid is not unreasonable. Such an overcall usually shows a few more points, but in the pass-out seat the requirement is lessened a little. Having said that, North's raise to 3NT is rather surprising, but his reasoning was simple: either the diamonds are coming in, making nine tricks likely, or they are not, making eight tricks unlikely. 3◇ was not an option as that would have been a transfer to hearts.

   Now to the play. The lack of diamond fit makes dummy distinctly unappetising. Any hope?

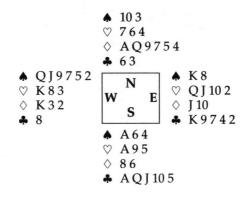

Dealer: West   Love All

A

```
                    ♠ 10 3
                    ♡ 7 6 4
                    ◇ A Q 9 7 5 4
                    ♣ 6 3
♠ Q J 9 7 5 2              ♠ K 8
♡ K 8 3          N        ♡ Q J 10 2
◇ K 3 2       W     E      ◇ J 10
♣ 8              S         ♣ K 9 7 4 2
                    ♠ A 6 4
                    ♡ A 9 5
                    ◇ 8 6
                    ♣ A Q J 10 5
```

South	**West**	**North**	**East**
	2♠ (weak)	Pass	Pass
2NT	Pass	3NT	All Pass

East overtakes the ♠Q lead with his ♠K. When you duck he continues with a second spade.

Obviously you cannot afford West to get the lead, otherwise four more spades will hit the deck. But, having said that, you will be forced to take the club finesse at some point.

A lazy declarer works out that he needs lots of luck and plays a diamond to the queen, a club back to that queen, a diamond to the ace, and another club to the jack. His luck runs out and he has to settle for two down.

Your best chance of making this contract is to bring in the diamonds – for this, you still need the finesse, but instead of taking it on the first round you need to take it on the second, so that your communications are intact. Thus you lead a diamond towards dummy, aiming to insert the ◇9. If West inserts a higher diamond, you have to change your plan, and play the queen, hoping for clubs to break as above.

Here West cannot put in a high diamond and the trick is won by East's jack. Win the heart switch and play your last diamond to the queen. Now cash the diamonds and, with fingers crossed, take a club finesse for tricks eight and nine.

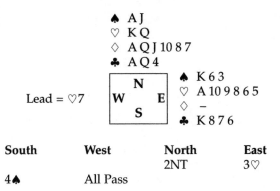

Q

Dealer: North   North-South Game

♠ A J
♡ K Q
♢ A Q J 10 8 7
♣ A Q 4

Lead = ♡7

♠ K 6 3
♡ A 10 9 8 6 5
♢ –
♣ K 8 7 6

South	West	North	East
		2NT	3♡
4♠	All Pass		

You win partner's ♡7 lead and return another heart, won in dummy (partner playing the ♡2). Declarer now plays the ♠J.

North was probably loath to display his opening 2NT bid which was rather misshapen as well as holding an extra point (although devaluing the king-queen doubleton is not unreasonable).

With 33 points between you and dummy, partner is unlikely to hold anything particularly useful. Is there a way to defeat the contract?

A

Dealer: North   North-South Game

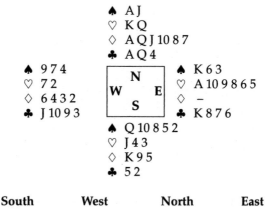

	♠ A J	
	♡ K Q	
	◇ A Q J 10 8 7	
	♣ A Q 4	

♠ 9 7 4   ♠ K 6 3
♡ 7 2   ♡ A 10 9 8 6 5
◇ 6 4 3 2   ◇ –
♣ J 10 9 3   ♣ K 8 7 6

♠ Q 10 8 5 2
♡ J 4 3
◇ K 9 5
♣ 5 2

South	West	North	East
		2NT	3♡
4♠	All Pass		

You win partner's ♡7 lead and return another heart, won in dummy (partner playing the ♡2). Declarer now plays the ♠J.

Why has declarer played the ♠J? To enable him to draw trumps whilst still holding the ♠A to protect against a heart ruff. If declarer held six spades and no ◇K, surely he would have tried the ♠A followed by the ♠J, hoping that partner had only two trumps.

Declarer's play is probably that of a man who holds the ◇K and this leaves you with no chance unless he has only five spades. This is unlikely, but perhaps he was unsure of the meaning of 3♠?

How should you defend? If you win and lead a third heart, partner will ruff and be overruffed with dummy's ace. Now declarer will try a diamond, which you will ruff and play a fourth heart. Declarer will ruff high, draw trumps and claim. No good.

To make sure that partner gets a ruff you should win the ♠K and return another trump. Now declarer is stuck – again he tries a diamond, but you ruff and now partner can make his trump too, since dummy is out of trumps and declarer still holds the ♡J.

Certainly you would expect South to hold a sixth spade for his bid, but if the only way to defeat the contract requires him to hold five, play him for five!

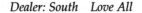

Dealer: South   Love All

Q

```
                        ♠  A 7 6
                        ♡  J 5 2
                        ◇  J
                        ♣  A Q 8 7 5 4
                            N
Lead = ♡7           W         E
                            S
                        ♠  K Q 8 2
                        ♡  K Q 4 3
                        ◇  K Q 9 5
                        ♣  2
```

South	West	North	East
1♡	Pass	2♣	Pass
2◇	Pass	3♡	Pass
3NT	Pass	4♡	All Pass

The ♡7 lead goes to East's ten and you win with the king.

4-4-4-1 hands are notoriously difficult to deal with, if only because partner always believes that your first-bid suit will have five cards. Here North might have thought a little harder about South's 3NT bid, but still it is not easy for him.

Anyway, although 3NT looks a lot easier, you have reasonable chances here. Win the ♡K and play a diamond. West wins his ◇A and plays a second trump, which again is run round to your hand and you win with the ♡Q.

It looks like East has the four trumps, how can you cope?

A

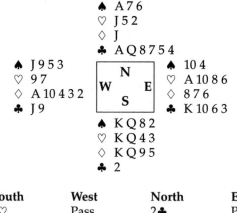

Dealer: South   Love All

♠ A 7 6
♡ J 5 2
◇ J
♣ A Q 8 7 5 4

♠ J 9 5 3
♡ 9 7
◇ A 10 4 3 2
♣ J 9

♠ 10 4
♡ A 10 8 6
◇ 8 7 6
♣ K 10 6 3

♠ K Q 8 2
♡ K Q 4 3
◇ K Q 9 5
♣ 2

South	West	North	East
1♡	Pass	2♣	Pass
2◇	Pass	3♡	Pass
3NT	Pass	4♡	All Pass

The ♡7 lead goes to East's ten and you win with the ♡K and play a diamond. West wins his ◇A and plays a second trump, which again is run round to your hand and you win with the ♡Q.

You have eight tricks and can easily make up the difference by taking ruffs. Should you cash any winners first?

Yes, if only because East might find himself endplayed later.

Cash the ♠A and ♠K, then the ◇KQ and ruff a diamond. If this holds you are almost there. You can play towards your remaining spade honour: if East ruffs you play small and have trump control and no other losers except for the ♡A; if he refuses to ruff or simply follows suit, you win the ♠Q and play the ♣A and another club – you score your tenth trick en passant. In the above hand East can overruff the fourth diamond, but now what? He is endplayed and after drawing a trump he has to lead a club. Of course, he might have had a spade, in which case you win that exit, and are home if spades are 3-3; if spades are 4-2 then you have no choice but to fall back on the now odds-on club finesse (East has only two clubs if he has four spades) – the spade loser goes on the second club.

Dealer: South   North-South Game

　　　　　　　　　♠ 10 9 3
　　　　　　　　　♡ Q J 7 2
　　　　　　　　　◇ A 5 3
　　　　　　　　　♣ K 5 3

Lead = ♠Q　　

```
      N
  W       E
      S
```

　　　　　　　　　♠ A 5
　　　　　　　　　♡ A K 9 6
　　　　　　　　　◇ Q J 7 6
　　　　　　　　　♣ Q 9 4

South	**West**	**North**	**East**
1NT (15-17)	Pass	3NT	All Pass

The ♠Q lead collects dummy's ♠3 and East's ♠2.

North had been advised not to use Stayman on 4-3-3-3 hands, and thus he leapt to 3NT. Unfortunately 4♡ has quite good chances as opposed to 3NT which … ?

Well, what can you make?

A

Dealer: South   North-South Game

```
            ♠ 10 9 3
            ♡ Q J 7 2
            ◇ A 5 3
            ♣ K 5 3
♠ Q J 8 7 4   ┌─────────┐   ♠ K 6 2
♡ 8 5 3       │    N    │   ♡ 10 4
◇ K 8 4       │ W     E │   ◇ 10 9 2
♣ 10 6        │    S    │   ♣ A J 8 7 2
              └─────────┘
            ♠ A 5
            ♡ A K 9 6
            ◇ Q J 7 6
            ♣ Q 9 4
```

South	West	North	East
1NT (15-17)	Pass	3NT	All Pass

The ♠Q lead collects dummy's ♠3 and East's ♠2.

There is very little hope, but in times of crisis desperate measures are called for.

Win the first trick confidently and play back a second spade.

This makes it more difficult for West than you might think. He may well suppose that you hold AKxx and are going for a ninth trick; even if it is not the ninth trick, West will never score his spade trick unless he takes it right away.

If he rises with the ♠J then the suit is blocked and declarer can prevail by making three diamonds tricks or two club tricks.

I certainly think that this line has a better chance of success than trying to get East to duck one round of clubs and for the ◇K to be singleton!

Q

Dealer: South   Love All

                     ♠ A J 6 5
                     ♡ A K
                     ◇ 9 7 6 4
                     ♣ Q J 5

                    ┌─────────┐   ♠ Q 10 4 3
                    │   N   │   ♡ Q 9 3
    Lead = ♣2   │ W   E │   ◇ Q 8 2
                    │   S   │   ♣ 10 9 4
                    └─────────┘

South	**West**	**North**	**East**
1♡	Pass	1♠	Pass
2◇	Pass	3◇	Pass
3♡	Pass	4♡	All Pass

Dummy is not quite what you expected to see – surely 3◇ is non-forcing? 3NT would appear to be the normal contract, and yet what on earth has declarer got for his bidding? Six hearts and four diamonds?

Whilst you are sitting and thinking about declarer's hand, he is quick to quell all of your fanciful theories: he wins trick one with the ♣Q, cashes the ♡AK, crosses to hand with the ◇A and plays a third trump to which partner follows with the ♡10!!

Odd bidding indeed. Any ideas?

A

Dealer: South   Love All

	♠ A J 6 5	
	♡ A K	
	◊ 9 7 6 4	
	♣ Q J 5	

♠ K 9 7		♠ Q 10 4 3
♡ 10 5 2	**N**	♡ Q 9 3
◊ J 10 3	**W E**	◊ Q 8 2
♣ K 8 6 2	**S**	♣ 10 9 4

	♠ 8 2	
	♡ J 8 7 6 4	
	◊ A K 5	
	♣ A 7 3	

South	West	North	East
1♡	Pass	1♠	Pass
2◊	Pass	3◊	Pass
3♡	Pass	4♡	All Pass

Declarer wins the ♣2 lead with the ♣Q, cashes the ♡AK, crosses to hand with the ◊A and plays a third trump to which partner follows with the ♡10!!

If declarer has four diamonds, he can have only one loser in the black suits (your partner does not usually underlead aces). So partner has to hold the ◊K. But notice partner's lead, showing at most four cards, putting declarer with a minimum of three clubs, and thus what appears to be a singleton spade. In this case partner needs to hold the ♣K too, leaving declarer with just the ♡J, ♣A and ◊AJ and a pretty bad suit – not an opening bid in anybody's book. It seems that if declarer has four diamonds this contract is going to make regardless of what you play.

But hold on, remember how strange the auction has been. In this kind of situation you do well to view the hand without the opponents' 'bad' bids. What if South has only three diamonds? If that is what you need to have a chance, then you should play on that premise.

Get rid of his entry to the long diamond by switching to a spade. Now you will make a trick in each suit. Without the switch, declarer will be able to dispose of one of his black-suit losers, using his ♠A as an entry to the thirteenth diamond.

Dealer: East   Love All

Q

```
                        ♠ 6 4
                        ♡ A K Q 4
                        ◇ Q J 8 7
                        ♣ 7 6 3
                        ┌─────────┐
                        │    N    │
        Lead = ♠8       │ W     E │
                        │    S    │
                        └─────────┘
                        ♠ 9 7
                        ♡ J 10 3
                        ◇ A 10 5
                        ♣ A Q 10 9 4
```

South	West	North	East
			Pass
1NT (12-14)	Pass	2♣	Pass
2◇	Pass	3NT	All Pass

West led the ♠8 to East's ace. East continued with the ♠K, followed by the ♠Q and ♠J before switching to the ◇3.

With just 23 points and a wide open suit, 'in the wrong contract' would be an accurate description of your predicament. South stretched his weak notrump to include a 'good 11' and after Stayman, North was not going to invite with 12 points!

Well, it seems someone is on your side because the spade suit is blocked, but that in a way is the least of your troubles – you have plenty of discards to make as well as a plan.

A

Dealer: East   Love All

```
                    ♠ 6 4
                    ♡ A K Q 4
                    ◇ Q J 8 7
                    ♣ 7 6 3
   ♠ 10 8 5 3 2   ┌─────────┐   ♠ A K Q J
   ♡ 8 5 2        │    N    │   ♡ 9 7 6
   ◇ K 9 6 4      │ W     E │   ◇ 3 2
   ♣ K            │    S    │   ♣ J 8 5 2
                  └─────────┘
                    ♠ 9 7
                    ♡ J 10 3
                    ◇ A 10 5
                    ♣ A Q 10 9 4
```

South	West	North	East
			Pass
1NT (12-14)	Pass	2♣	Pass
2◇	Pass	3NT	All Pass

West led the ♠8 to East's ace. East continued with the ♠K, followed by the ♠Q and ♠J before switching to the ◇3.

You must use all the information available, and on this hand the most important fact is East's original pass. He has turned up with 10 points in the spade suit alone, so he will not hold a minor-suit king.

It looks as though you must play for a minor miracle! Yes, you need a singleton king. There being more clubs in your combined hands (eight as against seven diamonds) this is the more likely option and where you should concentrate your efforts. This means not discarding a club from the North hand, for they are needed to pick up East's jack. (Notice how an early plan helps.)

You can throw a heart and a diamond from dummy because you need only three heart tricks if the clubs come in, and two diamonds can go from hand. Win the ◇A and cash the ♣A. It is time to feel guilty again as your atrocious bidding has paid dividends once more! Cross to the ♡A to take the first club finesse, then back to the ♡K for a second finesse, leaving you with all winners in hand.

Notice that if you bid badly, you must learn to play the cards well to compensate.

```
                          ♠ A K 9 3
                          ♡ A 5 4 3
                          ◇ A 4 3
                          ♣ A 4 3
        ♠ Q 7 6                           ♠ 10 5 2
        ♡ Q 7 6          N                ♡ K 8 2
        ◇ Q 10 7 6    W     E             ◇ K 5 2
        ♣ Q 10 7         S                ♣ K 5 2
                          ♠ J 8 4
                          ♡ J 10 9
                          ◇ J 9 8
                          ♣ J 9 8 6
```

South	West	North	East
1NT (weak)	Pass	2♣	Pass
2♠	Pass	3NT	All Pass

Four blind players were sitting playing bridge when they were called for tea. The auction had just finished. It is common for the blind, using Braille cards, to sort their cards into suits to make play more easy. When they left the table they each left four piles (one for each suit) on the table in front of them.

Unfortunately the host had a couple of mischievous children, who, while the players were eating and chatting, decided to play a little game – they rearranged the piles so that they looked as above – at least they were kind enough not to muddle the holdings in each suit, they simply moved some piles from player to player.

The bridge players arrived back, and straight away East professed to holding just twelve cards, and North fourteen.

The host quickly guessed what had happened and chased after her little imps. Meanwhile, the players were trying to remember their hands. Each player in turn stated that two of their suits were definitely correct, until South disagreed, saying that just one of his was correct. 'Well, I certainly had an ace,' continued West.

If I tell you that there was one quirk in the hand which was that no player held three of a kind in any denomination, can you replace the suits in their proper hands. (Hint: start with the four-card suits).

Finally, we can progress to the play. West makes the standard lead (4th highest). Who do you think will prevail? How should declarer play?

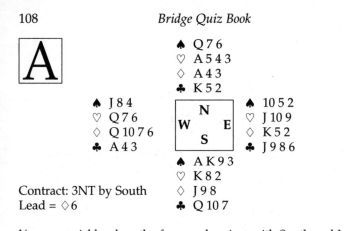

Contract: 3NT by South
Lead = ◇6

You can quickly place the four-card majors with South and North via the auction. What of the four-card minors? Say West has four clubs: his clubs have moved and his diamonds too (he has only three), therefore his majors remain. This fails because it has three sixes. Thus West must hold ◇Q1076 and ♣A43 (the only ace left), giving North ◇A43 since two suits must remain and his clubs and spades have already gone. Clearly East must hold the four clubs. Now there are two options: South holds either the ◇J or the ♡J (the ♣J has gone and his spades are known). Try the ♡J: then East holds ◇J98 and his original major suits but this would give him three eights. So South must holds the ◇J.

Back to North, who holds ♡A543 and ◇A43. He needs 12 points to bid 3NT, so he needs at least 4 more points. Without the ♣A he will need at least a point in spades, but the ♠J comes with the ♠4 which would give him three fours, so he must have ♠Q76. Since West needs one major-suit queen himself, he must hold the other, ♡Q76.

Nearly there. The ♡J109 must be East's, so his spades must stay the same. This gives West ♠J84 and, since South holds the ♡K and ♠K he cannot hold the ♣K, letting you finish the four hands as above.

The play: The lead goes to East's king, another diamond is ducked, and then a third diamond clears the suit. The defence have now established four tricks, so declarer cannot afford to yield another.

South will certainly need four spade tricks to go with two hearts and a diamond. There is only one place to go for the two necessary tricks and that is clubs. East must hold the ♣J. Play a club to the king and then finesse the jack on the way back. It is declarer who prevails by playing on clubs for two tricks to take his total to nine.

CHAPTER 6
Sacrifice

A sacrifice bid lands us in a contract which, although it may be going down, will not cost as much as the opponents making their contract. This aspect of the game can be a lot of fun, especially around the five level, when bidding can become a little hairy.

Sometimes, of course, we sacrifice over an opposing contract that would not have made; on the other side of the coin, sometimes our sacrifices make!

This chapter is filled with sacrifice bids: the good, the bad and the ugly.

Q   *Dealer: North   Love All*

♠ 7 4
♡ A 7 5 3
◇ K 8
♣ A K 9 5 3

	N	
W		E
	S	

South	West	North	East
		Pass	1♡[1]
1♠	2♣	4♠	Pass
Pass	Double	All Pass	

[1] four-card major

Lead = ?

You were in the process of making a delayed game raise when you were rudely interrupted. Having endplayed yourself in the auction you had no idea whether your side could make eleven tricks, so you decided to take the money, but how much?

A

Dealer: North   Love All

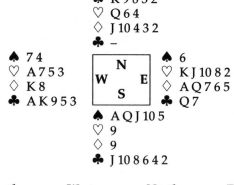

♠ K 9 8 3 2
♥ Q 6 4
♦ J 10 4 3 2
♣ —

♠ 7 4
♥ A 7 5 3
♦ K 8
♣ A K 9 5 3

N
W   E
S

♠ 6
♥ K J 10 8 2
♦ A Q 7 6 5
♣ Q 7

♠ A Q J 10 5
♥ 9
♦ 9
♣ J 10 8 6 4 2

South	West	North	East
		Pass	1♥
1♠	2♣	4♠	Pass
Pass	Double	All Pass	

Lead = ?

Where are their tricks coming from? *Trumps*, of course, and the fewer trumps they have the fewer tricks they will take.

Lead trumps twice (opening lead and when you get in with a diamond or a heart) and you restrict declarer to eight tricks.

Lead trumps once and declarer makes nine tricks.

Never lead trumps and declarer makes 4♠ doubled!

'I take a look at dummy by leading the ♥A,' says one West, but by then it is too late, for after a trump switch declarer plays the ♥Q and discards the ♦9 – scissors have snipped the entry to West's hand and East has no more trumps to lead, just one down.

When the opponents make overcalls it is important to show your fit quickly. It is best to show game-forcing hands with support for partner by making a cue-bid of the opponent's suit. Here you can bid 2♠ and East will have more idea of what to do later, probably pressing on to the eminently sensible 5♥. This time you were lucky because had you bid 5♥ North would have made a Lightner-type double, and South would not have taken long to take a club from his hand – club ruff, ♠A and a club ruff would have taken you down.

Dealer: South   North-South Game

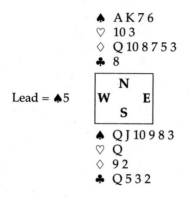

	♠ A K 7 6
	♡ 10 3
	◇ Q 10 8 7 5 3
	♣ 8

Lead = ♠5

	♠ Q J 10 9 8 3
	♡ Q
	◇ 9 2
	♣ Q 5 3 2

South	West	North	East
2♠	Double	4♠	Double
All Pass			

Slam appears to be on a club guess for the opposition, although that might be a bit of wishful thinking. They have only 24 points between them after all.

No, you would do better to aim for a save against their obvious game, but that means going just one down, because of the adverse vulnerability.

On the surface there are just four losers, but you have learnt to peer beneath the surface.

Any ideas?

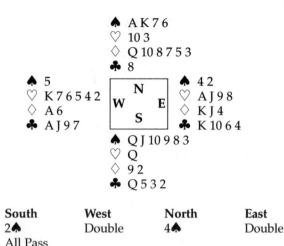

Dealer: South   North-South Game

South	West	North	East
2♠	Double	4♠	Double
All Pass			

West leads the ♠5.

If you try to ruff clubs in dummy, you will have a second club loser because the defence will draw a second trump. It is much better to establish diamonds, playing them right away to make sure you don't run out of entries.

Win the ♠Q and lead the ♢9. Say West wins, plays a heart to East's ace, and he plays a second trump. Win this and play another diamond. Win any return and you still have two entries to dummy – one to ruff a third diamond (establishing the suit) and the other to cash the diamonds. So you lose just one club, two diamonds and one heart, for one off and –200 against an easy 450.

Try anything else at trick two and you will see a crucial entry evaporate. For example, play a club. West will win and play a heart to East's ace. Now a trump means that declarer needs at least one diamond trick. But every time you lose a diamond the defence will play a club. You can establish the suit but you will have no entry to dummy to cash it.

East-West sold out rather meekly to 4♠, but at the vulnerability it might have been quite profitable, and against a less expert declarer than yourself +500 would have been ample recompense for any game.

Q

Dealer: East   East-West Game

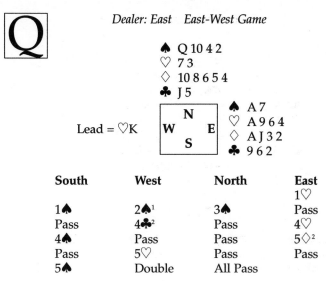

♠ Q 10 4 2
♡ 7 3
◇ 10 8 6 5 4
♣ J 5

Lead = ♡K

♠ A 7
♡ A 9 6 4
◇ A J 3 2
♣ 9 6 2

South	West	North	East
			1♡
1♠	2♠[1]	3♠	Pass
Pass	4♣[2]	Pass	4♡
4♠	Pass	Pass	5◇[2]
Pass	5♡	Pass	Pass
5♠	Double	All Pass	

[1] strong raise in hearts
[2] cue-bids

At trick two your partner leads a second heart which declarer ruffs. A spade to dummy's queen follows.

South has surely overbid? His partner made just one supporting call, and because of the favourable vulnerability, South could not resist making a sacrifice – once may have been a good idea, but the second … ? Well, it is up to you! How do you defend?

A

Dealer: East   East-West Game

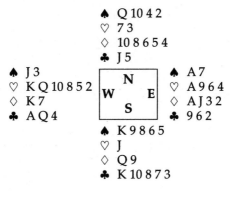

♠ Q 10 4 2
♡ 7 3
◇ 10 8 6 5 4
♣ J 5

♠ J 3
♡ K Q 10 8 5 2
◇ K 7
♣ A Q 4

♠ A 7
♡ A 9 6 4
◇ A J 3 2
♣ 9 6 2

♠ K 9 8 6 5
♡ J
◇ Q 9
♣ K 10 8 7 3

South	West	North	East
			1♡
1♠	2♠	3♠	Pass
Pass	4♣	Pass	4♡
4♠	Pass	Pass	5◇
Pass	5♡	Pass	Pass
5♠	Double	All Pass	

West leads the ♡K and continues at trick two with a second heart which declarer ruffs. A spade to dummy's queen follows.

You need four more tricks to take your total to six and give you 800 points as compensation for the 650 you might have got in 5♡, but should you set your sights so low?

It seems to be a straight choice between the minors, but there are a couple of factors to take into account. If you have top tricks in the two minors, it will be easy, but you might need to establish a trick by some other means – a trump promotion possibly. If you play diamonds first when West makes his promoted trump he will be endplayed, forced to give a ruff and discard or lead a club round to declarer's king.

Win the ♠A and play a *high* club in order to deny an honour; now partner cannot go wrong. He will win his queen or ace, cash the other club and then the ◇K and continue a diamond. You will win and play a third diamond, allowing West to make his ♠J (now or later).

So you get seven tricks and +1100 – about what South deserved!

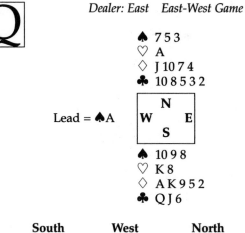

Q

Dealer: East   East-West Game

♠ 7 5 3
♡ A
♢ J 10 7 4
♣ 10 8 5 3 2

Lead = ♠A

N
W   E
S

♠ 10 9 8
♡ K 8
♢ A K 9 5 2
♣ Q J 6

South	West	North	East
			1♡
2♢	4♡	5♢	Double
All Pass			

West continues with the ♠K dropping East's queen, then the ♠J on which East discards a low heart, followed by a heart switch.

I think partner has bid a little too much on his 5-count! With five losers off the top and trumps to deal with, the only thing that could be worse is to find that 4♡ was not making!

How are you going to turn a bad situation into a good one?

A

Dealer: East   East-West Game

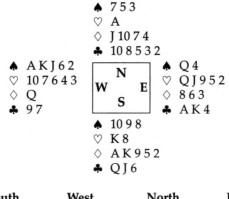

♠ 7 5 3
♡ A
◇ J 10 7 4
♣ 10 8 5 3 2

♠ A K J 6 2
♡ 10 7 6 4 3
◇ Q
♣ 9 7

N
W   E
S

♠ Q 4
♡ Q J 9 5 2
◇ 8 6 3
♣ A K 4

♠ 10 9 8
♡ K 8
◇ A K 9 5 2
♣ Q J 6

South	West	North	East
			1♡
2◇	4♡	5◇	Double
All Pass			

West leads the ♠A, ♠K, ♠J. East plays the ♠Q on the king and discards a low heart on the jack. West switches to a heart.

If diamonds are 2-2 you have four winners against 4♡, so you have to hope that they are 3-1. This looks likely; as West holds ♠ AKJxx, he probably has five hearts to justify his jump to game without mentioning the spade suit.

So, win ♡A and run the ◇J – oops! – West wins his singleton queen.

It might look as though you are short of entries to dummy, but that is just an illusion. Win the ♡A, cash the ◇A and if nothing falls, ruff the ♡K, and now take the diamond finesse.

Once you have picked up the trumps, you just have to give up two club tricks, going three down for a cost of –500; a struggle, but in the end worth it, since East-West's 4♡ is worth 620.

Notice that West could have taken you four off by playing clubs and taking a ruff. This did not look attractive because he could see you would be short of dummy entries and was anxious not to do any of your work for you.

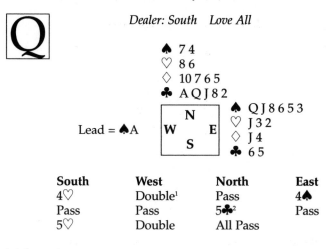

Dealer: South   Love All

Q

♠ 7 4
♡ 8 6
◇ 10 7 6 5
♣ A Q J 8 2

Lead = ♠A

♠ Q J 8 6 5 3
♡ J 3 2
◇ J 4
♣ 6 5

South	**West**	**North**	**East**
4♡	Double¹	Pass	4♠
Pass	Pass	5♣²	Pass
5♡	Double	All Pass	

¹ take-out
² values in clubs and support for hearts

North has little defence outside clubs, and this is what he is trying to tell his partner – it looks as though 4♠ will probably make and he wants to give partner a chance to bid 6♡ over 5♠ if necessary. His partner was not put to the test, but looking at your hand you are still unsure whether or not this is a sacrifice!

What does partner need to know? How do you play to trick one?

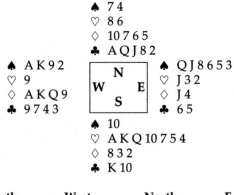

	South	**West**	**North**	**East**
	4♡	Double	Pass	4♠
	Pass	Pass	5♣	Pass
	5♡	Double	All Pass	

Lead = ♠A

In situations like this, when declarer is likely to hold solid trumps and quite possibly a solid side suit, it is imperative to cash out all available top winners. To do that successfully you must give count whenever possible. With a six-card spade suit you should play high-low to show an even number and the clearest card has to be the ♠8.

The ♠Q does not give count, it simply implies holding the jack and partner does not need to know that on this hand. The ♠J would be seen as strange especially if, as here, declarer played the ten; partner may switch to a club expecting you to ruff it!!

When partner sees the ♠8 he will switch to his top diamonds and you again give count – the ◇J on the first round. It is now easy for him to play three rounds of diamonds, after which he can go back to spades just in case!

Four tricks is two off and +300; not as good as +420, but better than –750, which would have been the result if partner had not switched to diamonds at trick two.

Dealer: West   Love All

```
              ♠ 7 6 2
              ♡ 6 4
              ♢ A 9 5 3
              ♣ A K 7 6
                    N
Lead = ♠K     W         E
                    S
              ♠ Q 9 5
              ♡ A Q
              ♢ 6 4
              ♣ Q J 10 9 8 5
```

South	West	North	East
	1♡	Pass	2♡
3♣	3♢¹	3♡²	Pass
3NT	Pass	Pass	4♡
Pass	Pass	5♣	Pass
Pass	Double	All Pass	

¹ general game-try (not showing diamonds)
² asking partner to bid 3NT with a heart stop

East plays the ♠3 at trick one and West switches to the ♢K.

Not the most ordinary of auctions! Partner was quite right to bid 3♡, for it seems that the chances in 3NT are very good – nine tricks on a heart lead – but was he right then to bid 5♣ over 4♡? He probably bid it hoping it might make but as it is you have to hope it is a good sacrifice.

On enquiring into your opponents' signalling methods, you are advised that the opening lead of a king asks for count.

If 4♡ is making you can afford two down, can you manage that?

A

Dealer: West   Love All

```
                    ♠ 7 6 2
                    ♡ 6 4
                    ◇ A 9 5 3
                    ♣ A K 7 6
   ♠ A K 8 4         ┌─────────┐      ♠ J 10 3
   ♡ K J 8 5 2       │    N    │      ♡ 10 9 7 3
   ◇ K 7          W  │         │  E   ◇ Q J 10 8 2
   ♣ 4 2             │    S    │      ♣ 3
                     └─────────┘
                    ♠ Q 9 5
                    ♡ A Q
                    ◇ 6 4
                    ♣ Q J 10 9 8 5
```

South	West	North	East
	1♡	Pass	2♡
3♣	3◇	3♡	Pass
3NT	Pass	Pass	4♡
Pass	Pass	5♣	Pass
Pass	Double	All Pass	

West leads the ♠K. East plays the ♠3 at trick one and West switches to the ◇K.

You have one club, one diamond and at least one heart trick against 4♡, so you require West to hold the ♡K for the sacrifice to be real rather than phantom. Do you still have a play for nine tricks?

You need to keep East off lead, so ducking the diamond switch must be right. Now you can win any return, draw trumps, cash the ◇A and ruff a diamond. You simply need to ruff enough diamonds to leave West void in that suit. Now play the ♡A followed by the ♡Q and West is left on lead to give a ruff and discard, or to yield a trick to your ♠Q.

You eventually lose two spades, one heart and one diamond for –300, against –420 for 4♡. None of this compares particularly well against +400 for 3NT but were you ever likely to play there?

Notice how the count given by East at trick one did not help you too much, but on many hands it is of the utmost importance to watch the signals on the opening lead – it is rare for a defender to lie when faced with a direct question from his partner.

Try your hand at making a few decisions about sacrifice bidding. Sacrifices can be some of the more profitable contracts in bridge – unfortunately they are profitable for both sides depending on the skill of the bidder and often the skill of the defence.

You are West in each of the following auctions:

(A) *Dealer: West   Love All*
- ♠ A K 8 6 5 4
- ♡ 7
- ◇ A 8 6
- ♣ 7 6 5

South	West	North	East
	1♠	Double	3♠[1]
4♡	?		

[1] stretch raise – a raise to 2♠ without the double

(B) *Dealer: North   Game All*
- ♠ J 8 7 6 5
- ♡ 5
- ◇ J 9 7 6 3 2
- ♣ 4

South	West	North	East
		1♡	1♠
2♠[1]	?		

[1] A good raise to 3♡ or better

(C) *Dealer: North   Love All*
- ♠ K 8 6 4
- ♡ 7 4
- ◇ K Q 8 5
- ♣ Q 3 2

South	West	North	East
		1♡	2♠[1]
3♠[2]	?		

[1] weak jump overcall, 6-10
[2] A good raise to 4♡ or better

(A) An easy one to start with. Partner has shown a relatively weak hand with four spades. If you play in 4♠ you can lose six tricks at most. You might even make 4♠ on a good day, but will usually go one, or perhaps two, off. 4♠ is a good two-way shot because if you make you want to be there and if you go down 4♡ is likely to be making. Partner held:

♠ Q J 7 2　♡ 8 6 5　◇ K 9 7 4　♣ 9 2.

You lost two clubs, one heart and one diamond in 4♠ doubled for –100. In 4♡ declarer would lose one spade and the ◇AK for –420. A very good sacrifice.

(B) Another two-way shot here. Even with just your two jacks 4♠ could be making – give partner the ♠AK and a singleton diamond for example. You have no defence against a 4♡ contract at all. However bad partner's hand is you are very unlikely to go more than two down – remember if partner's hand is bad he will hold good spades and thus your only losers will be your own two singletons and the number of diamonds in partner's hand (although if he holds three you might just lose two if the suit splits 2-2).

This hand is definitely worth 4♠ – it is not unlikely that you will record +790 because who will guess that you hold a hand like this. Partner held:

♠ A K 10 9 2　♡ 7 6 4　◇ 8 4　♣ K Q 8

Not ideal with the ♣KQ rather wasted opposite your singleton, but still you lose just four tricks for what would have been –200. However, South bid on to 5♡ which, with the two club honours offside, was one off for +100! 4♡, of course, cannot fail.

(C) You have excellent support for partner's suit, but a distinct lack of ruffing values. The ability to ruff is what partner will be looking for – that is what made the two above hands so attractive. You do have a doubleton heart, but partner is unlikely to have more than two hearts himself, so that won't help. Steer clear of this one – it is not as if you have no defence. If you keep quiet they might bid to a doomed slam. Partner held:

♠ A Q J 9 5 3　♡ 8 2　◇ J 3　♣ 8 7 4

Unsurprisingly most of partner's points are in his suit. In 4♠ you would lose two hearts, one diamond and three clubs for -500 – too much against the -420 or -450 for their game.

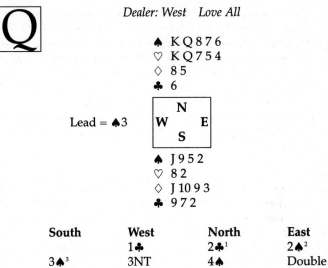

Dealer: West   Love All

♠ K Q 8 7 6
♡ K Q 7 5 4
◇ 8 5
♣ 6

Lead = ♠3

```
      N
  W       E
      S
```

♠ J 9 5 2
♡ 8 2
◇ J 10 9 3
♣ 9 7 2

South	West	North	East
	1♣	2♣[1]	2♠[2]
3♠[3]	3NT	4♠	Double
All Pass			

[1] Michaels, showing length in both majors
[2] some club support and a spade stop   [3] pre-emptive

East wins the lead with the ♠A and returns the ♠4.

The Michaels cue-bid is quite a popular use of the direct bid of the opponent's suit – it comes up a lot more often than the super-strong hand which it was originally used to show. South's brave 3♠ bid gave North the chance to do something rather unusual, make a sacrifice bid against 3NT. It looks as though partner was right – five clubs, three diamonds and two aces gives them ten tricks – but only if you can keep your losers down to five.

A

Dealer: West　Love All

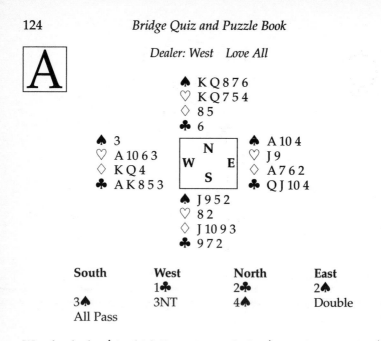

	South	**West**	**North**	**East**
		1♣	2♣	2♠
	3♠	3NT	4♠	Double
	All Pass			

West leads the ♠3 which East wins with the ♠A and returns the ♠4.

The good lead might well have ruined your chances. If trumps break 3-1 you will be able to ruff only one heart in dummy, so if the hearts do not break you will have to hope that West holds the ♡A.

You must insert the ♠9 on this trick. If West has the ♠10 there is no problem because the trumps have split 2-2 (you can take two ruffs in hand), but if they split 3-1 you are now in hand and able to play a heart up to the king. When this holds, you can play a spade back to hand drawing the last trump, and play another heart up to the queen. Whether West takes his ace or not, he will make just one heart trick. That leaves you with eight tricks, losing one trump, one heart, two diamonds and a club – two down for –300.

Notice that if you don't put in the ♠9, you are an entry short. You cannot afford to play the ♡K from dummy, because West wins and crosses to his partner's hand so that East can play a third trump – now that you have wasted one of your top hearts you have to lose a second heart trick.

A successful sacrifice against 3NT! In fact, playing Pairs, East-West would have to overcall 4♠ with 4NT (to play!) to get their best score.

Q

Dealer: South   Game All

```
                    ♠ Q 9 7 3
                    ♡ 8 7
                    ◇ J 10 9 4 3
                    ♣ A 2
    ♠ A J 10
    ♡ K 10 9 6 3 2        N
    ◇ A K 5          W         E
    ♣ 10                  S
```

South	West	North	East
2♠ (weak)	3♡	4♠	5♣[1]
5♠	Double	All Pass	

[1] showing clubs but also suggesting support for hearts

You lead the ♣10, won by dummy's ace. Next comes a spade to the king, partner discarding a heart.

There do not appear to be too many losers in hearts, so 5♡ is probably a make and you would like to get 5♠ three down to compensate.

Can you find a route to five tricks?

A

Dealer: South   Game All

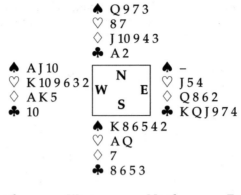

♠ Q 9 7 3
♡ 8 7
◇ J 10 9 4 3
♣ A 2

♠ A J 10
♡ K 10 9 6 3 2
◇ A K 5
♣ 10

N
W   E
S

♠ –
♡ J 5 4
◇ Q 8 6 2
♣ K Q J 9 7 4

♠ K 8 6 5 4 2
♡ A Q
◇ 7
♣ 8 6 5 3

South	West	North	East
2♠ (weak)	3♡	4♠	5♣
5♠	Double	All Pass	

West leads the ♣10, won by dummy's ace. Next comes a spade to the king, partner discarding a heart.

What tricks do you hope to make? Two trumps, one heart, one diamond and one club.

How is declarer going to stop you? By an endplay or by cross-ruffing.

That is enough! Win the ♠A and exit with the ♠J, for precisely the two reasons stated above – cut down declarer's ruffing potential and remove one obvious card that will result in your being endplayed.

Now declarer is stuck – he will try a diamond, but you win and play your last trump. Declarer has just one entry to dummy and cannot establish his diamonds. He eventually loses one diamond, one heart, two spades and two clubs for +1100 – a good piece of work.

Q Solve the clues and fill in the answers below. When you have finished that, the title of a famous story and its author will appear down the shaded left-hand column. The other letters should be transposed into the diagram at the bottom of the page using the numbered squares, to give a quotation from this work.

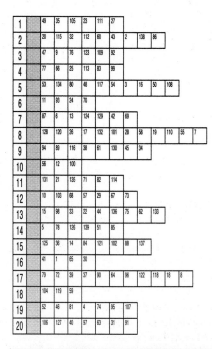

1. Deliberately misbid.
2. Mad – not good at notrumps!
3. Severely criticised for Six Clubs at sea.
4. Hearts always at battle with diamonds in this gallery.
5. Two hundred to the bad guys.
6. Silly coup.
7. Opening rule.
8. A film, a card and a cook!
9. Don't play the top card!
10. Peter!...........Peter!
11. Act V is over, now we have to exit.
12. Yarborough.
13. Film and Bridge Star.
14. Splendid play.
15. Best place to ruff, quickly noted.
16. Tops.
17. Card face down, he asked "...
18. At night the diamond ace fetched a French and English king!
19. Partnership in opposition.
20. In a row between King, Queen and Jack.

1	2	3		4	5	6	7		8	9	10	11		12	13	14	15	16	17	18
	19	20	21		22	23	24	25	26	27		28	29	30		31	32	33	34	
35	36	37	38		39	40	41	42	43		44	45	46		47	48	49	50		
51	52	53	54		55	56	57	58	59	60	61	62	63	64	65	66		67	68	69
70	71	72		73	74	75	76	77	78	79		80	81	82	83	84	85	86		
87	88	89	90	91	92		93	94	95	96	97	98	99		100	101		102	103	
104	105	106		107	108	109	110	111		112	113	114		115	116	117	118	119	120	
121	122	123		124	125	126		127	128	129	130	131		132	133		134	135	136	137
138	139																			

1	**P**	SYCHED
2	**U**	NBALANCED
3	**S**	LAMMED
4	**H**	AYWARD
5	**K**	ISSOFDEATH
6	**I**	DIOT
7	**N**	INETEEN
8	**Q**	UEENOFHEARTS
9	**U**	NDERLEAD
10	**E**	CHO
11	**E**	NDPLAY
12	**N**	INEHIGH
13	**O**	MARSHARIF
14	**F**	INESSE
15	**S**	HORTHAND
16	**P**	EAKS
17	**A**	NYQUESTIONS
18	**D**	ARK
19	**E**	ASTWEST
20	**S**	EQUENCE

'Ace wins!' said Hermann, and showed his card. 'Your queen has lost,' said Tchekalinsky gently. Hermann started: indeed, instead of an ace there lay before him the Queen of Spades.

The last lines of Pushkin's short story, 'Queen of Spades'.

CHAPTER 7
Moysian Fits

A Moysian fit is a 4-3 fit, named after Alphonse Moyse Jr, who had a propensity for playing in such contracts.

The most common reason for wanting to play in a Moysian fit is when 3NT is ruled out because a suit is wide open. At Pairs in particular a 4-3 major fit may be chosen in preference to five of a minor.

If you are going to play in 4-3 fits, you will have to sharpen up your card play, for the contracts can be quite difficult to manage. For the defence the question is often whether to lead trumps to restrict the short hand's ruffing value, or to lead a side suit in order to shorten the long trump hand.

Q

Dealer: South   Love All

♠ J 10 7 2
♡ 9 8 4 3
◇ 3
♣ A K 10 2

South	West	North	East
1NT (15-17)	Pass	2♣	Pass
2♡	Pass	3◇	Pass
3♡	Pass	4◇	Pass
4♠	All Pass		

What is your lead?

If you lead a club partner plays the ♣Q. What do you continue when dummy comes down with:

        ♠ K 9 4 3   ♡ 6   ◇ A K 7 6 5 4   ♣ 7 5

What is your plan?

Dealer: South   Love All

```
                    ♠ K 9 4 3
                    ♡ 6
                    ♦ A K 7 6 5 4
                    ♣ 7 5
   ♠ J 10 7 2                      ♠ 6 5
   ♡ 9 8 4 3         N             ♡ Q J 7 5
   ♦ 3           W       E         ♦ J 10 8 2
   ♣ A K 10 2        S             ♣ Q J 8
                    ♠ A Q 8
                    ♡ A K 10 2
                    ♦ Q 9
                    ♣ 9 6 4 3
```

South	West	North	East
1NT (15-17)	Pass	2♣	Pass
2♡	Pass	3♦	Pass
3♡	Pass	4♦	Pass
4♠	All Pass		

West leads the ♣K on which partner plays the ♣Q.

You expect dummy to hold six diamonds and four spades and be relatively short in clubs. The opponents certainly seem to be playing in a 4-3 fit, after South's reluctance to bid 3♠ on the third round. That means that you can shorten the long trump hand by leading clubs right away, and give your side trump control. This looks like a hand where declarer will try to set up diamonds rather than cross-ruff, so by taking control of the trump suit you should be able to foil his plan.

Lead the ♣K and, when partner plays the ♣Q, play a small club to his jack, and he will continue with a third club forcing dummy to ruff. Declarer tries a diamond to his queen and a diamond back, but you continue your excellent defence by ruffing. This foils declarer's planned cross-ruff. A fourth club now makes things impossible for declarer. He can ruff with the ♠9, but has no entry to the established diamonds without losing another ruff. He tries a sly heart, but partner inserts the queen. Now declarer admits defeat, accepting one off.

Any non-club lead allows declarer to throw one of his club losers and puts him in control.

Dealer: South   Love All

```
                        ♠ Q J 6
                        ♡ 7 6 3
                        ◇ A K 8 5 3
                        ♣ 5 2
                     ┌─────────┐
                     │    N    │
Lead = ♠2         W  │         │  E
                     │    S    │
                     └─────────┘
                        ♠ A K 10 7
                        ♡ 10 4
                        ◇ 9 7
                        ♣ A K 9 7 3
```

South	West	North	East
1♣	Pass	1◇	Pass
1♠	Pass	2♡¹	Pass
2♠	Pass	3♠	Pass
4♠	All Pass		

¹ fourth-suit forcing

North-South bid very well to this game. The bidding was natural up to North's 2♡ bid – this was fourth-suit forcing, asking South to describe his hand a little more, especially with respect to a heart stop. South, without a heart stop, was unable to bid notrumps, so rebid his good spades.

Now North felt he was worth a raise, and South did not hesitate to bid game, knowing the power of his honour cards.

There are two problems: (1) How should you play at trick one; (2) Which suit should you try to ruff first?

Dealer: South Love All

```
                    ♠ Q J 6
                    ♡ 7 6 3
                    ◇ A K 8 5 3
                    ♣ 5 2
    ♠ 9 5 4 2         ┌─────┐        ♠ 8 3
    ♡ K Q 9 5         │  N  │        ♡ A J 8 2
    ◇ J 6 4        W  │     │  E     ◇ Q 10 2
    ♣ Q 4            │  S  │        ♣ J 10 8 6
                     └─────┘
                    ♠ A K 10 7
                    ♡ 10 4
                    ◇ 9 7
                    ♣ A K 9 7 3
```

South	West	North	East
1♣	Pass	1◇	Pass
1♠	Pass	2♡	Pass
2♠	Pass	3♠	Pass
4♠	All Pass		

West leads the ♠2.

Four top tricks outside trumps, so you need six trump tricks, which should be easy enough as long as you avoid an early overruff. You do best to force out one of the danger cards (the ♠9 and ♠8) at trick one, by playing small in dummy. This would work especially well if West had led away from the ♠98, but as it is East puts in the ♠8.

The only trump that can now lose is South's ♠7 and the best play is to ruff with that card as early as possible before West can make a disadvantageous discard. The first rule of cross-ruffing is to cash your outside winners first. So cash both ace-kings before ruffing a diamond.

So, win East's ♠8 with the ♠A and cash the ♣AK, then the ◇AK. Now the moment of truth, ruff a diamond small – everybody follows and you can cross-ruff high, for ten tricks.

Notice what happens if you try a club ruff first: ♠A, ◇AK, ♣AK, then a club ruff on which West discards a diamond. Now when you ruff a diamond with the ♠7 West can overruff.

Q

Dealer: South   Love All

> ♠ A K 8 3
> ♡ 10 8 2
> ◇ 7 6
> ♣ A 6 3 2

Lead = ♡ K

```
        N
  W         E
        S
```

> ♠ J 6 2
> ♡ 7
> ◇ A K Q J 5 4
> ♣ 10 5 4

South	West	North	East
1◇	2♡ (weak)	Double[1]	3♡
Pass	Pass	Double[1]	Pass
3♠	Pass	4♠	All Pass

[1] take-out

After the ♡ K has held West switches to the ♠10 which you run to your jack.

If you will open light then you have to suffer the consequences. To be fair, South has a reasonable hand and with such a strong suit his opening bid is not unreasonable. West made a weak jump overcall and North made a take-out double (suggesting four spades). East kept up the pre-emption by raising to 3♡ and North still did not want to sell out – after all if his partner had any kind of normal opening bid then the hand should rightfully be theirs. South, in desperation tried 3♠ and North, perhaps unwisely, raised to 4♠.

One advantage of such an auction is that the defenders have no idea of the type of hand you have. How do you play after winning the ♠J?

Dealer: South   Love All

```
                        ♠ A K 8 3
                        ♡ 10 8 2
                        ◇ 7 6
                        ♣ A 6 3 2
        ♠ 10 4                           ♠ Q 9 7 5
        ♡ K Q 9 6 5 3       N            ♡ A J 4
        ◇ 8 2           W       E        ◇ 10 9 3
        ♣ K 8 7             S            ♣ Q J 9
                        ♠ J 6 2
                        ♡ 7
                        ◇ A K Q J 5 4
                        ♣ 10 5 4
```

South	West	North	East
1◇	2♡ (weak)	Double	3♡
Pass	Pass	Double	Pass
3♠	Pass	4♠	All Pass

West leads the ♡K which holds, and switches to the ♠10 which you run to your jack.

You have been given a chance so do not let it go! If you can draw trumps you are home, and as long as spades break no worse than 4-2 it should be easy. Simply play a second round of trumps and duck. The defence have no recourse because you can still ruff a heart in hand.

Had you not ducked this round of trumps, instead playing the ♠A and ♠K, then you would have been unable to cope with heart leads. As it is you make three trumps, six diamonds and the ♣A.

You should not be allowed to make this contract, but how was West supposed to know what to do? He knows you have a singleton heart and quite possibly short trumps, and thus a trump seemed reasonable – it was only wrong when you turned up with six good diamonds!

It is all too easy to settle in 3NT playing Duplicate Pairs, only to find that there is one suit wide open – this is often excusable, for the pursuit of the extra ten points is important.

Playing Teams there is little excuse. It is your job to find the best game, not to extract a measly ten bonus points from playing in notrumps; exploration is the name of the game.

The hands below are from Teams matches, where the auctions quickly reached a hopeless 3NT. See if you can tell the East-West pair what went wrong and suggest a better auction.

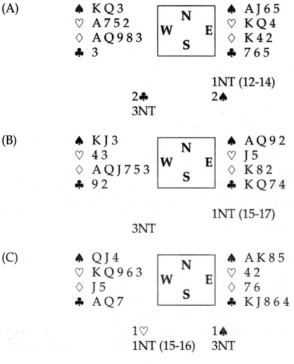

(A)

♠ K Q 3
♡ A 7 5 2
◇ A Q 9 8 3
♣ 3

♠ A J 6 5
♡ K Q 4
◇ K 4 2
♣ 7 6 5

	1NT (12-14)
2♣	2♠
3NT	

(B)

♠ K J 3
♡ 4 3
◇ A Q J 7 5 3
♣ 9 2

♠ A Q 9 2
♡ J 5
◇ K 8 2
♣ K Q 7 4

| | 1NT (15-17) |
| 3NT | |

(C)

♠ Q J 4
♡ K Q 9 6 3
◇ J 5
♣ A Q 7

♠ A K 8 5
♡ 4 2
◇ 7 6
♣ K J 8 6 4

| 1♡ | 1♠ |
| 1NT (15-16) | 3NT |

	(A)		1NT (12-14)
		2♣	2♠
		3♦	3♡
		3♠	4♦
		4♠	

West has obvious doubt about the club suit, so why not take the time to find out if partner does too? 3♦ shows West's hand and is game-forcing. East has denied four hearts by his response to Stayman so can bid 3♡ and West can show his good spades. It is easy for East to avoid 3NT now and he should continue his description with 4♦. With his partner known to have most of his values outside clubs, West might find his way to the diamond slam, but that would take a little more machinery. Here they are happy to avoid 3NT and settle in their safe Moysian fit, 4♠.

	(B)		1NT (15-17)
		3♦	3♠
		4♠	

West has two wide-open suits, and should certainly explore the possibility of a suit contract. Over 3♦ East will bid a good holding, not necessarily a four-card suit, but after 3♠ (missing out 3♡) West knows their side should be playing in a suit. He gives partner the option of playing in spades (West cannot have four spades because he did not use Stayman) – after all he has shown six diamonds already. East wisely accepts West's offer of a Moysian fit, guessing that there might be two hearts and the ♣A to lose.

	(C)	1♡	1♠
		1NT (15-16)	3♣
		3♠	3NT
		4♣	4♠

Not so easy, this one. The initial 1♠ response is OK and often works better on this mediocre hand-type than 2♣, but over partner's 1NT response there is no excuse for forgetting the clubs altogether. Over partner's 3♠ preference it is difficult not to bid 3NT but with no diamond guard at all partner is able to bid on himself, showing club support. Now it is easy to pick the Moysian fit of 4♠.

Q

Dealer: South   Game All

♠ A 7 6 3 2
♡ K Q 6
◇ 7
♣ A 7 4 3

Lead = ♠Q

```
      N
  W       E
      S
```

♠ –
♡ A J 10 7
◇ A K 10 9 5 3
♣ K 10 8

South	West	North	East
1◇	Pass	1♠	Pass
2♡	Pass	3♣[1]	Pass
3◇	Pass	3♡	Pass
4♣[2]	Pass	4♠[2]	Pass
4NT[3]	Pass	5♣[4]	Pass
6♡	All Pass		

[1] fourth-suit forcing   [2] cue-bids   [3] Roman Key Card Blackwood
[4] zero or three of the five 'aces'

A very well-bid slam. The bidding was natural until 3♣ which was
fourth-suit forcing. South rebid his diamonds to suggest extra length
and then North showed delayed support for hearts, suggesting three
cards only. South cue-bid 4♣ (avoiding his shortage in partner's suit)
and North accepted the slam try with 4♠.

South bid Roman Key Card Blackwood (knowing that North held
the ♠A). After the response which showed three of the five 'aces',
South bid the slam in hearts on the strength of his good
intermediates.

After all that, you had better ensure that you make twelve tricks.

Dealer: South   Game All

```
                    ♠ A 7 6 3 2
                    ♡ K Q 6
                    ◇ 7
                    ♣ A 7 4 3
        ♠ Q J 10         N         ♠ K 9 8 5 4
        ♡ 8 5 3      W       E      ♡ 9 4 2
        ◇ Q J 6 4 2      S         ◇ 8
        ♣ J 6                      ♣ Q 9 5 2
                    ♠ –
                    ♡ A J 10 7
                    ◇ A K 10 9 5 3
                    ♣ K 10 8
```

South	West	North	East
1◇	Pass	1♠	Pass
2♡	Pass	3♣	Pass
3◇	Pass	3♡	Pass
4♣	Pass	4♠	Pass
4NT	Pass	5♣	Pass
6♡	All Pass		

West led the ♠Q.

Diamonds and hearts are the important suits. You can deal with both suits breaking 4-2; and if hearts are 3-3 you can cope with diamonds 5-1.

Win the ♠A discarding a club. Cash the ◇A, ruff a diamond high, club to the ♣K, followed by a second high ruff. Now draw three rounds of trumps. If diamonds are 4-2 the suit is now good, so just play it out and whichever defender has a trump left can take it when he wishes. If diamonds are 5-1 and trumps have broken, just concede a diamond and claim the remainder.

Notice that you must ruff high straight away to give youself that extra chance when diamonds are 5-1.

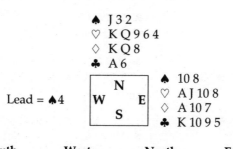

Dealer: North   Love All

Q

♠ J 3 2
♡ K Q 9 6 4
◇ K Q 8
♣ A 6

Lead = ♠4

```
      N
 W         E
      S
```

♠ 10 8
♡ A J 10 8
◇ A 10 7
♣ K 10 9 5

South	West	North	East
		1♡	Pass
1♠	Pass	1NT (15-16)	Pass
2◇	Pass	2♠	All Pass

Declarer plays low from dummy at trick one and wins your ♠10 with his ♠Q. He continues with a spade to dummy's ♠J and then the ◇K.

The title of this chapter will certainly help you with this one, but your partner's lead and the bidding should have made you think of a 4-3 fit anyway.

When, as responder, you hold a hand not strong enough to call at the two level, you reply 1NT or in a four-card major. It is quite obvious that South holds such a hand, and his distribution is not suitable for 1NT.

The play at trick three backs up this premise, as rather than continue drawing trumps declarer has switched to his side suit. Can you see a way to hold declarer to seven tricks?

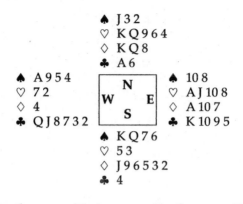

Dealer: North   Love All

A

	♠ J 3 2	
	♡ K Q 9 6 4	
	◇ K Q 8	
	♣ A 6	

♠ A 9 5 4		♠ 10 8
♡ 7 2	N	♡ A J 10 8
◇ 4	W E	◇ A 10 7
♣ Q J 8 7 3 2	S	♣ K 10 9 5

	♠ K Q 7 6	
	♡ 5 3	
	◇ J 9 6 5 3 2	
	♣ 4	

South	West	North	East
		1♡	Pass
1♠	Pass	1NT (15-16)	Pass
2◇	Pass	2♠	All Pass

West leads the ♠4 to the ♠10 and ♠Q. He continues with a spade to dummy's ♠J and then the ◇K.

To stop declarer enjoying his diamonds you must hold up your ace for two rounds. On the second round partner discards the ♡7.

Now declarer is in trouble. If he plays another diamond you win and play a club. He wins this in dummy, but cannot get back to hand without shortening his trumps. Say he plays a heart. You win the ♡K with your ace, partner playing the ♡2 and play a club. If declarer ruffs this, West will ruff your diamond winner, cash the ♠A and run his clubs, but if declarer discards on the club, it has the same effect. West cashes the ♠A and exits with another club which declarer ruffs, but West has the rest. Declarer makes just six tricks – three trumps, two diamonds and a club.

If declarer switches to the ♡K after the ◇K is ducked, you win and play a club, won by dummy's ace. The position is more or less the same as above.

So you did not manage to find a way to restrict declarer to seven tricks, but I am sure six will do!

Q

Dealer: South   Game All

♠ A J 7 4 3
♡ 8 6 5 4
♢ 2
♣ K 8 2

Lead = ♡3

```
    N
W       E
    S
```

♠ 10 5
♡ A K Q
♢ J 7 6
♣ A Q 10 5 3

South	West	North	East
1♣	1♢	1♠	2♢
Pass	Pass	Double[1]	Pass
2NT	Pass	3♣	Pass
3♡	Pass	4♡	All Pass

[1] take-out

The ♡3 lead goes to the ♡4, ♡9 and your ♡A. You play a diamond which West wins and continues a second trump the ♡7 to the ♡8, ♡2 and your ♡Q.

4♡ was well bid. South felt he had no other bid than 2NT in response to his partner's double, but with a minimum shapely hand North gave preference to clubs. With a lot more than he might have had South went on by bidding his strong three-card heart suit and North raised to game. 5♣ is not a bad contract either, but both game contracts struggle on trump leads. Unfortunately that is exactly what you have received.

From East's play in the trump suit (the ♡9 on the first round and the ♡2 on the next) it appears that the hearts are splitting 2-4. What chance now?

Dealer: South   Game All

```
                        ♠ A J 7 4 3
                        ♡ 8 6 5 4
                        ◇ 2
                        ♣ K 8 2
     ♠ Q 9 6 2                          ♠ K 8
     ♡ 7 3           ┌─────────┐        ♡ J 10 9 2
     ◇ A Q 9 8 5 3   │    N    │        ◇ K 10 4
     ♣ 6             │ W     E │        ♣ J 9 7 4
                     │    S    │
                     └─────────┘
                        ♠ 10 5
                        ♡ A K Q
                        ◇ J 7 6
                        ♣ A Q 10 5 3
```

South	West	North	East
1♣	1◇	1♠	2◇
Pass	Pass	Double	Pass
2NT	Pass	3♣	Pass
3♡	Pass	4♡	All Pass

The ♡3 lead goes to the ♡4, ♡9 and your ♡A. You play a diamond which West wins and continues the ♡7 to the ♡8, ♡2 and your ♡Q.

If East has four trumps you have no control and have to hope that he has long clubs as well. Win the second trump and ruff a diamond. Play a club to the ace, ruff the last diamond, cash the ♠A and the ♣K and then take the club finesse. Making ten tricks. The contract is easy once the decision about trumps has been made.

Notice how East's trump play gave away the position – on the first round he used a high trump to force a high card from declarer, on the second round he knew the position and so played low. He would have done better to follow with the ♡10 on the second round – now things are more difficult for declarer.

The play in a seven-card fit often centres around whether trumps are 3-3 or 4-2; sometimes there is no choice but often you have to make the all important decision, and it is vital to look for every clue.

Dealer: North   Love All

Q

```
            ♠ Q J 7
            ♡ 8 4 3
            ◇ A Q J 9
            ♣ K 6 3
                  N
Lead = ♡K    W       E
                  S
            ♠ A K 10 3
            ♡ 7 5
            ◇ 8 3
            ♣ A Q J 10 4
```

South	West	North	East
		1NT (12-14)	Pass
2♣	Pass	2◇	Pass
3♣	Pass	3◇	Pass
3♠	Pass	4♠	All Pass

West leads the ♡K followed by the ♡Q to East's ace and a third heart.

After a somewhat convoluted sequence including Stayman you have arrived at what appears to be a rather good spot. South's 3♣ bid was game-forcing (rather than the oft-used weak take-out in old-fashioned Acol), showing at least five clubs and a four-card major.

West has found your weak spot. Can you make your well-bid game?

A

Dealer: North   Love All

```
                    ♠ Q J 7
                    ♡ 8 4 3
                    ◇ A Q J 9
                    ♣ K 6 3
    ♠ 6 4              ┌─────────┐         ♠ 9 8 5 2
    ♡ K Q J 10 2       │    N    │         ♡ A 9 6
    ◇ 6 5 4           │ W     E │         ◇ K 10 7 2
    ♣ 9 7 5           │    S    │         ♣ 8 2
                       └─────────┘
                    ♠ A K 10 3
                    ♡ 7 5
                    ◇ 8 3
                    ♣ A Q J 10 4
```

South	West	North	East
		1NT	Pass
2♣	Pass	2◇	Pass
3♣	Pass	3◇	Pass
3♠	Pass	4♠	All Pass

West leads the ♡K followed by the ♡Q to East's ace and a third heart.

You have ten tricks on top, so there can only be one problem: trump control. That is the design behind West's lead. Rather than a trump to stop you ruffing, he is positively encouraging you to ruff.

If the defenders encourage you to do something, always think twice about it. Here if you ruff you give East trump control, and endanger your contract. Best is to discard a diamond on the third round of hearts. Now the defence are helpless: a fourth heart is ruffed high in dummy, and any other lead gives you your original ten tricks.

The odds are with a 4-2 trump break so it is important to keep control and avoid ruffing.

Avoiding all the pitfalls, you have made a good game when many will be one off in 3NT.

Dealer: North   East-West Game

```
              ♠ A J 10
              ♡ 7 2
              ◇ A 8 4 3
              ♣ A 8 4 2
                   N
Lead = ♠3     W         E
                   S
              ♠ K Q 8 7
              ♡ 9 6 3
              ◇ K J 7
              ♣ K Q 9
```

South	West	North	East
		1◇	Pass
1♠	Pass	2♠	Pass
2NT	Pass	3♣	Pass
3◇	Pass	4♠	All Pass

Once again the defence kick off to the best lead – a heart ruff would
have been your tenth trick, but it seems likely that that plan will be
foiled. How else will you make your game?

A

Dealer: North   East-West Game

```
                        ♠ A J 10
                        ♡ 7 2
                        ◇ A 8 4 3
                        ♣ A 8 4 2
        ♠ 6 3                              ♠ 9 5 4 2
        ♡ K J 8 5          N               ♡ A Q 10 4
        ◇ Q 10 6 2    W         E          ◇ 9 5
        ♣ 7 6 3            S               ♣ J 10 5
                        ♠ K Q 8 7
                        ♡ 9 6 3
                        ◇ K J 7
                        ♣ K Q 9
```

South	West	North	East
		1◇	Pass
1♠	Pass	2♠	Pass
2NT	Pass	3♣	Pass
3◇	Pass	4♠	All Pass

West leads the ♠3.

There are plenty of chances for extra tricks in the minor suits, it is just a matter of combining your chances. You should give up on the option of a heart ruff as the defence will clearly not allow it.

You cannot draw trumps yet, for then if you lose a trick you will lose three hearts as well. To keep all your options open, you should take an immediate finesse in diamonds. You must not cash a top diamond first though, for that may open the way for ruffs.

When West wins his ◇Q he plays another trump. Now it is time to draw trumps (discarding a heart from dummy) and cash your minor-suit winners, hoping that at least one suit breaks 3-3. It is clubs that give you your tenth trick eventually. This line allowed you to make if either minor was 3-3 or if the ◇Q was right. A well-timed hand, for as suggested, the ◇A followed by a finesse would have yielded a diamond ruff as the fourth defensive trick.

Solve the straightforward clues and you will find the title of this puzzle running down the shaded left-hand column of the grid. The remaining letters need to be transposed to the hand pattern underneath and the instructions therewith.

Each of the cards are in word form, i.e. NINE for 9, and the letters transposed make up these cards in random order.

1 Damp
2 Sporting offence
3 Overtly
4 Repercussion
5 Single
6 Fairly
7 Shine
8 Interrogate
9 More than one one
10 Not essential
11 Jump out
12 Fastener
13 Film certificate

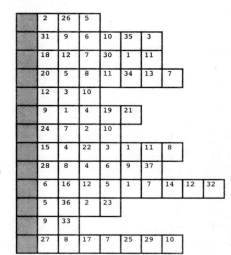

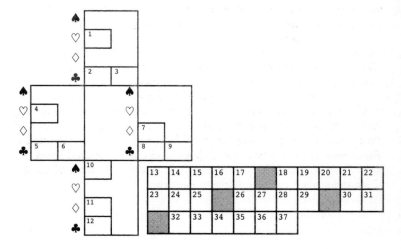

1	**D**	**ANK**
2	**O**	**FFSIDE**
3	**U**	**PFRONT**
4	**B**	**ACKWASH**
5	**L**	**ONE**
6	**E**	**VENLY**
7	**S**	**HEEN**
8	**Q**	**UESTION**
9	**U**	**NITIES**
10	**E**	**XTRANEOUS**
11	**E**	**JECT**
12	**Z**	**IP**
13	**E**	**IGHTEEN**

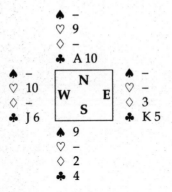

SOUTH PLAYS THE NINE OF SPADES

And now a double squeeze operates: West cannot let go the ♡10 so must discard a club, but now dummy discards the ♡9 (its job done), and East falls under the squeeze's spell. He cannot discard his diamond because that will allow declarer to win his ◇2! So he too discards a club, but now declarer can win the last two tricks with dummy's clubs.

CHAPTER 8
Goulash

A goulash is a bridge hand that is dealt in a particular way, which increases the chances of extreme distributions occurring. It results in some crazy bidding and some crazy play. It is a deal used in some rubber bridge circles after a passed-out hand.

Do not moan about bad breaks and distribution, because that is exactly why we play a goulash in the first place.

Q

Dealer: West   Love All

```
              ♠ 7
              ♡ –
              ◇ K Q J 10 7 5
              ♣ A K J 9 8 4
                          ♠ A 4 2
              ┌─────────┐ ♡ J 9 6 2
Lead = ♠Q     │    N    │ ◇ 9 8 3 2
              │ W     E │ ♣ 5 3
              │    S    │
              └─────────┘
```

South	West	North	East
	1♠	4NT[1]	Pass
5♣	Pass	6♣	All Pass

[1] pick a minor

Looking at dummy, it seems North got a little carried away in the bidding – 4NT was fine, but raising to slam thereafter was pushing it!

Having said that, you had better make sure he pays his dues. You win your ace but how do you continue?

Dealer: West　Love All

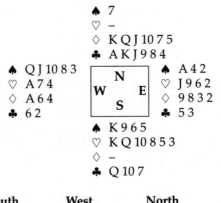

	North		
♠ 7			
♡ –			
◇ K Q J 10 7 5			
♣ A K J 9 8 4			

West   East
♠ Q J 10 8 3   ♠ A 4 2
♡ A 7 4   ♡ J 9 6 2
◇ A 6 4   ◇ 9 8 3 2
♣ 6 2   ♣ 5 3

South
♠ K 9 6 5
♡ K Q 10 8 5 3
◇ –
♣ Q 10 7

South	**West**	**North**	**East**
	1♠	4NT	Pass
5♣	Pass	6♣	All Pass

West leads the ♠Q to your ace.

On first analysis it seems that if declarer holds the ◇A this slam is going to make (the ♣Q is right). Except of course if partner holds a diamond void. On this reasoning then you would lead a diamond.

Think again! If partner had a void diamond, declarer would hold three to the ace, but South has already said he has better clubs than diamonds in the auction. This would put him with say, Q10xx, leaving partner with one card in the minors, and the ♡AKQ to justify his opening bid. This does not quite fit!

No, you must assume that partner holds the ◇A and now the worry is that declarer is void in diamonds.

If he has four trumps there is nothing to be done, but if he has just three, a trump return will leave him a ruff short. Play back the ♣3.

As you can see, with his ten points declarer knows that West holds both red aces for his opening bid. When he wins your trump switch, he will try to establish hearts, but he cannot quite do it, and when the ◇A does not fall in two rounds, he has to go one off.

A nice defence, but I think most of the congratulations have to go to partner who managed to avoid leading either of his red aces, which would have given the slam away.

Dealer: South   East-West game

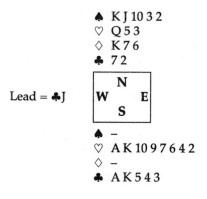

♠ K J 10 3 2
♡ Q 5 3
◇ K 7 6
♣ 7 2

Lead = ♣J

```
      N
  W       E
      S
```

♠ –
♡ A K 10 9 7 6 4 2
◇ –
♣ A K 5 4 3

South	**West**	**North**	**East**
3♡	Double	4♡	4♠
6♡	Double	Pass	Pass
Redouble	All Pass		

East plays the ♣Q at trick one.

As usual the goulash results in a game of bluff and double-bluff. South opens 3♡, knowing that the auction will not stop there and that he might get doubled to his advantage later. Once his partner has supported him South is in no doubt that the odds favour him making at least 6♡.

Does someone have a singleton club? If so, who and how do you play? Remember, you did redouble!

A

Dealer: South   East-West Game

```
                    ♠ K J 10 3 2
                    ♡ Q 5 3
                    ◇ K 7 6
                    ♣ 7 2
    ♠ A Q 5          ┌───────────┐      ♠ 9 8 7 6 4
    ♡ J 8            │     N     │      ♡ —
    ◇ A Q J       W  │           │  E   ◇ 10 9 8 5 4 3 2
    ♣ J 10 9 8 6      │     S     │      ♣ Q
                    └───────────┘
                    ♠ —
                    ♡ A K 10 9 7 6 4 2
                    ◇ —
                    ♣ A K 5 4 3
```

South	West	North	East
3♡	Double	4♡	4♠
6♡	Double	Pass	Pass
Redouble	All Pass		

West leads the ♣J, East playing the ♣Q.

If there is a singleton club you will have to ruff two clubs, so cannot afford to draw more than one trump. Furthermore you will have to duck the second club to avoid a top club being ruffed away.

This is how South's thought processes worked. If he found a 1-1 trump break he would be cold for twelve tricks, so he cashed the ♡A to find that the trumps were 2-0. Still not knowing who held the singleton club (if anybody) he did not want to risk the ♣K, so he ducked a club. But now West won and continued with his second trump, leaving South a trick short.

Ouch! –200 instead of +1320 and a game.

You do not need to draw even one trump. You should start by winning the first club and playing a small club back. If West wins and continues a club you ruff with the ♡Q, play a heart to the ace and ruff your last small club in dummy. Finally you return to hand with a diamond ruff to draw the last trump and claim.

Strangely with such a powerful pair of hands, if East holds a singleton club and doubleton heart, there is no way of making this contract.

Dealer: East   Love All

```
            ♠ A 4
            ♡ A Q 5
            ◇ A 9 5 2
            ♣ A J 6 3
```

```
                N
Lead = ♠2    W     E
                S
```

```
            ♠ J 9 8 6
            ♡ J 10 8 7 4 3
            ◇ –
            ♣ Q 4 2
```

South	West	North	East
			1♠
Pass	1NT	Double	4◇
4♡	5◇	Double	Pass
5♡	Double	All Pass	

Here we go again! Partner's original double is ostensibly take-out of
spades although it can show a very strong balanced hand –
unfortunately you forgot about the last possibility and hence have
found yourself in a lovely contract! You had better make this one or
partner might have something to say.

What shape do you think East is? He is obviously not that strong
so surely he must be exceptionally distributional, perhaps 6-6? West's
lead looks like a singleton so East certainly has six spades.

Can you find a route to save face?

Dealer: East   Love All

```
                    ♠ A 4
                    ♡ A Q 5
                    ♢ A 9 5 2
                    ♣ A J 6 3
    ♠ 2                           ♠ K Q 10 7 5 3
    ♡ K 9 6 2        N            ♡ –
    ♢ J 8 3       W     E         ♢ K Q 10 7 6 4
    ♣ K 10 9 7 5     S            ♣ 8
                    ♠ J 9 8 6
                    ♡ J 10 8 7 4 3
                    ♢ –
                    ♣ Q 4 2
```

South	West	North	East
			1♠
Pass	1NT	Double	4♢
4♡	5♢	Double	Pass
5♡	Double	All Pass	

West leads the ♠2.

It certainly seems most likely that East's distribution is 6-6, particularly when you remember that West's 1NT is not a very strong bid.

You do best to win the lead and continue with another spade (West discarding a club), setting the stage for a cross-ruff. East is almost bound to continue with a top diamond which you ruff and lead the ♣Q to the king and ace. Now the ♢A throwing a club and the ♣J. Here you discover the truth when East discards a diamond. Now you ruff a diamond and play a spade leaving West helpless. If he throws his penultimate club, you ruff small, ruff a club, and now West is forced to underruff in front of dummy when you play your last spade. All he can make is his ♡K. He might force you to ruff with the ♡Q by ruffing in with the ♡6, but you continue the torture by again ruffing a club back to hand and leading the last spade. The ♡9 forces the ace, but all he can make is the ♡K.

Vindicated again – what a great bid that 5♡ was!

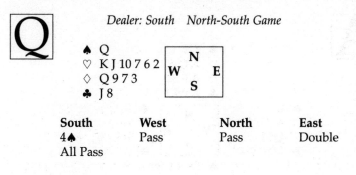

Dealer: South   North-South Game

♠ Q
♡ K J 10 7 6 2
◇ Q 9 7 3
♣ J 8

South	West	North	East
4♠	Pass	Pass	Double
All Pass			

Lead = ?

Double was primarily penalties and you decided with your mixed values to pass. Now what do you lead?

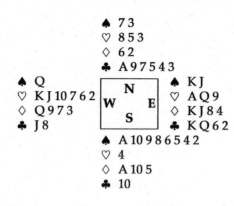

Dealer: South   North-South Game

♠ 7 3
♡ 8 5 3
◇ 6 2
♣ A 9 7 5 4 3

♠ Q
♡ K J 10 7 6 2
◇ Q 9 7 3
♣ J 8

N
W   E
S

♠ K J
♡ A Q 9
◇ K J 8 4
♣ K Q 6 2

♠ A 10 9 8 6 5 4 2
♡ 4
◇ A 10 5
♣ 10

South	**West**	**North**	**East**
4♠	Pass	Pass	Double
All Pass			

Lead = ?

At this vulnerability South should have some kind of realistic hope of making his contract.

With no idea what is the right lead and no ace to enable you to look at dummy, you are probably best to lead a trump. It is relatively safe and sometimes has a very pleasant side-effect.

Here the side-effect is to stop an all-important ruff in dummy. Without that ruff declarer has to lose two diamonds to go with one trump and one heart – one down.

Your side's lack of aces make bidding at the five level wrong. Note that even 4♡ would fail because of a club ruff.

Dealer: South   North-South Game

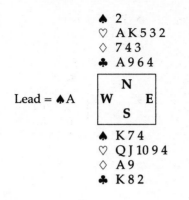

Lead = ♠A

```
              ♠ 2
              ♡ A K 5 3 2
              ◇ 7 4 3
              ♣ A 9 6 4
           N
        W     E
           S
              ♠ K 7 4
              ♡ Q J 10 9 4
              ◇ A 9
              ♣ K 8 2
```

South	West	North	East
1♡	4♠	5♡	All Pass

At trick two West switches to the ◇10. Can you find a way home?

Dealer: South   North-South Game

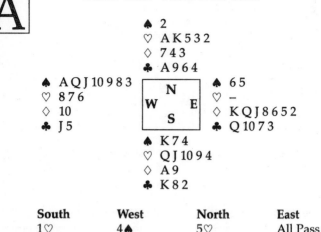

	A	B	C	

South	**West**	**North**	**East**
1♡	4♠	5♡	All Pass

West leads the ♠ A, then switches to the ◇ 10.

On the surface it appears that you have a loser in each of the minor suits to add to the ♠ A.

But there is one chance that might save you. You need to find West with a singleton diamond and either defender with a doubleton club, so that you can endplay him. Whoever has the longer hearts is the one to play for the shorter clubs. Remember that although West has shown long spades you need East to have seven diamonds!

Win the ◇ A and draw trumps. When East shows out on the first round, West is your man. Continue by cashing your club winners finishing in hand. Now cash the ♠ K and continue with another spade, discarding two diamonds from dummy. West must win and has only spades left. He perforce continues with a spade which you can ruff in dummy, discarding your losing club from hand. Now a cross-ruff collects the rest of the tricks.

Had it been East who had held the longer trumps you would have played the same way, but after cashing your club winners you would discard a diamond on the ♠ K and ruff a spade. Now if East had started with a doubleton club a diamond would endplay him, and North would ruff the forced diamond return, South discarding a club (South now having only trumps left).

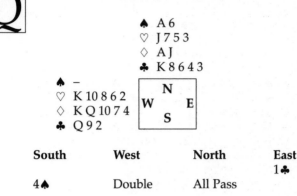

♠ A 6
♡ J 7 5 3
◇ A J
♣ K 8 6 4 3

♠ —
♡ K 10 8 6 2
◇ K Q 10 7 4
♣ Q 9 2

South	West	North	East
			1♣
4♠	Double	All Pass	

You lead the ◇K won by dummy's ace. Declarer returns the ◇J, partner playing the ◇9 then ◇6.

Your double was a two-way action, although your hand is rather more suited for take-out than penalties! Dummy is looking rather good, and you have a feeling that it might take some time to work out the score for this one.

You must do what you can with what little you have. Partner appears to have a doubleton diamond as well as dummy. Can that help?

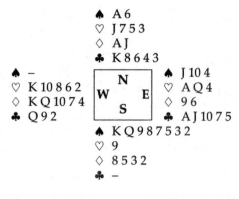

A

♠ A 6
♡ J 7 5 3
◇ A J
♣ K 8 6 4 3

♠ –
♡ K 10 8 6 2
◇ K Q 10 7 4
♣ Q 9 2

♠ J 10 4
♡ A Q 4
◇ 9 6
♣ A J 10 7 5

♠ K Q 9 8 7 5 3 2
♡ 9
◇ 8 5 3 2
♣ –

South	West	North	East
			1♣
4♠	Double	All Pass	

West leads the ◇K won by dummy's ace. Declarer returns the ◇J, East playing the ◇9 then the ◇6.

If you simply return a diamond now, declarer is likely to ruff high, return to hand with a ruff and ruff a second diamond. Partner can overruff this fourth diamond, but by then that might be with a trump trick.

You need to draw a round of trumps and so must put partner in. Which suit is more likely to stand up?

Partner has bid a natural 1♣ so that puts him with at the very minimum four clubs, but quite likely five. A heart certainly looks the better shot. (If declarer turns up with the ♡A, 4♠ is starting to look impregnable.)

So you play a small heart which partner wins with his ace and returns the ♠J. Now declarer is stuck. If he wins in dummy, he cannot take a diamond ruff without an overruff. But if he wins in hand and ruffs a diamond with the ♠A, he then has a trump loser. Declarer has to lose two diamonds (the ◇K and his long diamond), one heart and either a trump, an overruff or a third diamond. He goes one off.

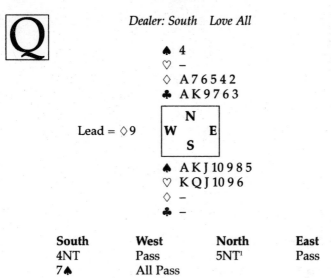

Dealer: South   Love All

Q

```
              ♠ 4
              ♡ —
              ◇ A 7 6 5 4 2
              ♣ A K 9 7 6 3
                    N
Lead = ◇9     W         E
                    S
              ♠ A K J 10 9 8 5
              ♡ K Q J 10 9 6
              ◇ —
              ♣ —
```

South	West	North	East
4NT	Pass	5NT[1]	Pass
7♠	All Pass		

[1] two aces

You win the opening lead with the ◇A and East plays the ◇K.

An Acol 4NT opening is a rare breed indeed, and here South decided that all he needed was the ♡A to make a grand slam. Usually responder bids specific aces but unfortunately with two aces the response is 5NT, and now South's knowledge of the mechanics of the 4NT opening were used up! He had no idea how to find out which aces his partner held. So with a 2-1 on chance of finding him with the ♡A, he bid the grand slam.

When dummy came down, South had various emotions quickly following each other: aagh no ♡A, wow no heart at all! His final thought was that perhaps he had overestimated the strength of his spade suit.

A

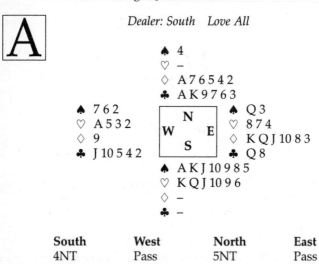

Dealer: South   Love All

	South	West	North	East
	4NT	Pass	5NT	Pass
	7♠	All Pass		

Declarer wins the ◇9 lead with the ◇A, East playing the ◇K.

You are going to need West to hold the ♡A, but because you can't draw even one trump, you also need to get rid of some hearts early. Win the three minor-suit winners, discarding hearts.

Now consider West's shape. His lead and East's play suggests he has short diamonds, five or less clubs, and you need him to hold at most four hearts. How do you get back to hand? West might have a singleton diamond (when he will have three or more spades), but if that is so he must not hold the ♠Q as you need that to fall.

So you can safely ruff a diamond with the ♠8. Now take a ruffing heart finesse. This is ducked twice and covered the third time. Ruff, cross back to hand with a club ruff and draw trumps, laughing at your good fortune when the ♠Q does indeed fall.

Why so much trouble over West's shape? Try ruffing a club back to hand at trick four. If you do that East will throw a heart and eventually be able to ruff the third heart before West's ace has been dislodged. It does not matter if West discards hearts because he must hold the ace.

You needed plenty of luck on this hand, but also plenty of thought. Well worked out!

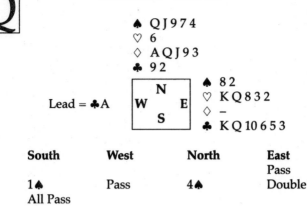

Dealer: East   Game All

Q

```
              ♠ Q J 9 7 4
              ♡ 6
              ◇ A Q J 9 3
              ♣ 9 2
                              ♠ 8 2
                  ┌───────┐   ♡ K Q 8 3 2
                  │   N   │   ◇ —
Lead = ♣A         │ W   E │   ♣ K Q 10 6 5 3
                  │   S   │
                  └───────┘
```

South	West	North	East
			Pass
1♠	Pass	4♠	Double
All Pass			

Partner has not responded to your call! Your double is surely a clear trumpet blast, rather like a *Lightner* double of a slam. As a passed hand it is too much to suggest that you would be able to double this without some feature in your hand, especially when dummy puts down such an impressive hand.

Basically your double suggested that you could ruff the first round of a suit, and is a request for partner to lead his longest suit, or the suit he thinks you can ruff.

To be fair your double was optimistic, for you did need partner to hold an entry, but of course his ♣A would have been just that!

Is there any way to rescue the situation?

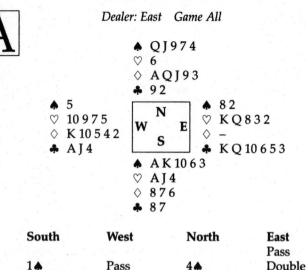

South	West	North	East
			Pass
1♠	Pass	4♠	Double
All Pass			

West leads the ♣A.

You have to hope that partner understood your double, but just wanted to take a look at dummy. So, to take this down you need another entry to partner's hand. The ♡A is unlikely, but perhaps your only chance unless partner holds the ♣J. How will you know if he holds the ♣J?

The way to find the best defence to this contract is to give partner the chance to signal his ♣J. Underneath his ♣A, play the ♣K, promising the ♣Q. Now if he holds the ♣J he will play back his lowest diamond. You will ruff and confidently play back a small club. He can now give you your second diamond ruff to defeat the contract.

If partner does not hold the ♣J or ♡A he will play back a middle diamond and you will cash your ♣Q, settling for three defensive tricks – not brilliant but better than giving an overtrick by underleading your club honours and finding declarer with the ♣J!

Of course, if partner held the ♡A he would play back his highest diamond asking for the higher suit. Now you would beat 4♠ by two, but you might have made a few tricks in hearts yourselves – twelve to be exact!

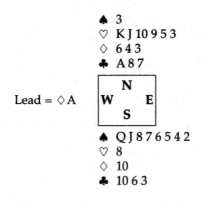

Dealer: South   Love All

♠ 3
♡ K J 10 9 5 3
♢ 6 4 3
♣ A 8 7

Lead = ♢ A

N
W   E
S

♠ Q J 8 7 6 5 4 2
♡ 8
♢ 10
♣ 10 6 3

South	West	North	East
4♠	Pass	Pass	Double
All Pass			

West continues at trick two with the ♢ K.

Yes, I am afraid you were responsible for the opening bid! Slightly aggressive, but this is a goulash, and it is likely other players have long suits to get off their chests too. This certainly made it difficult for them.

After West's diamond continuation you are still in with a chance of a good save. How do you take advantage?

Dealer: South   Love All

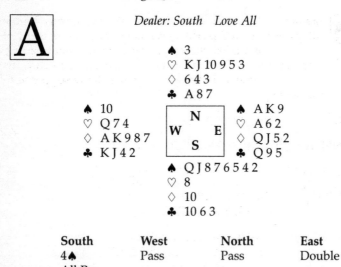

South	West	North	East
4♠	Pass	Pass	Double
All Pass			

West leads the ◇A, followed by the ◇K.

After West's helpful defence you might be able to establish a heart trick before the ♣A is knocked out. Ruff the second diamond and play a heart to the jack (East is likely to have the ♡A for his double). East wins his ace and plays back a club to West's ♣J. Duck, win the second round and cash the ♡K discarding your last club. Now a trump from dummy on which East plays the ♠9. How should you play?

A 4-0 break is too much and you can forget about a 3-1 break offside (if West had ♠AK10 he would have doubled himself). You must concentrate on East holding three trumps. West can hold singleton ten, ace or king. So, is it two to one on to play small?

Think of the bidding. You already know that West has the ◇AK and the ♡Q. What about clubs? Surely East would have switched to a high club if he had the ♣KQ, so West must have a second honour in that suit. The most East can have is ten points outside spades, so he is likely to have both honours.

All angles studied, you go up with the ♠Q which holds the trick. You concede two trump tricks and are two down for –300.

There are usually one or two clues somewhere; it is just a question of knowing where to look.

Below is the convention card of a very famous bridge player who would probably not have come across many of the conventions on the card, hence he has muddled up their spellings. Could you try and sort out his name, his partner's name and the conventions they are supposed to be playing.

NAME	BURY STONE CELL
PARTNER NAME	ROLE CHANGERS
BASIC SYSTEM	COLA
NOTRUMP	A LIVE BAR
Responses	NASTY MA, STAR FERNS

OPENING TWOS		
	2♣	CAGE FORMING
	2♦	COOL RED TUMULI
	2♡	NEAR FLYN
	2♠	ANT ART

Opening 3 Bids	ME PET VIPER
Opening 4 Bids	I CAN'T FAX ART'S HOUSE
1NT overcall	GRENADER
2NT overcall	MANOR

Defence to pre-empts: Weak Twos   THE TACK
Weak Threes   BEFINISH   Higher bids   TUBA OPENLY LED

Defence to 1NT   PROP IN STATION
Defence to strong 1 club   SHARP CURES

DOUBLES	PUN KITS, THEN GIRL, PERSON VIES
Jump overcalls	WAKE
SLAM conventions	BERGER, COLD WAR BOOK MAN
Other Conventions	BONE SHELL
LEADS	FIGHT THE HOURS, RENT TONGS
SIGNALS	SOUND WIPED

NAME	ELY CULBERTSON
PARTNER NAME	CHARLES GOREN
BASIC SYSTEM	ACOL
NOTRUMP	VARIABLE
Responses	STAYMAN, TRANSFERS

OPENING TWOS		
	2♣	GAME FORCING
	2♦	MULTICOLOURED
	2♡	FLANNERY
	2♠	TARTAN

Opening 3 Bids	PREEMPTIVE
Opening 4 Bids	SOUTH AFRICAN TEXAS
1NT overcall	GARDENER
2NT overcall	ROMAN

Defence to pre-empts:	Weak Twos	HACKETT
Weak Threes FISHBEIN	Higher bids	PENALTY DOUBLE

Defence to 1NT	PINPOINT ASTRO
Defence to strong 1 club	SUPER CRASH
DOUBLES	SPUTNIK, LIGHTNER, RESPONSIVE
Jump overcalls	WEAK
SLAM conventions	GERBER, ROMAN BLACKWOOD
Other Conventions	LEBENSOHL
LEADS	FOURTH HIGHEST, STRONG TEN
SIGNALS	UPSIDE DOWN

CHAPTER 9
Slams

We finish with everyone's favourite: the glory of the slam. There is something special about a slam, not just the points that it gains, but the little extra buzz it gives. To bid all the way there and then take the twelfth or thirteenth trick is always exhilarating.

Here there are a number of different slams – small and grand. See if you can finish with a bang.

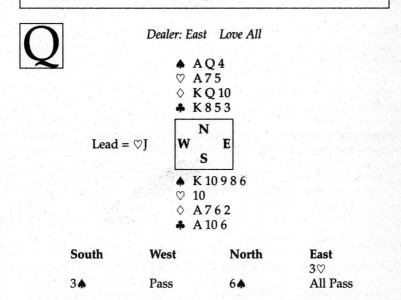

Q

Dealer: East   Love All

♠ A Q 4
♡ A 7 5
◇ K Q 10
♣ K 8 5 3

Lead = ♡J

N
W   E
S

♠ K 10 9 8 6
♡ 10
◇ A 7 6 2
♣ A 10 6

South	West	North	East
			3♡
3♠	Pass	6♠	All Pass

You win the lead and cash the ♠A and ♠K, but East discards a heart on the second.

Not the most cultured of sequences, but you are where you want to be, that is until East shows out on the second trump! Is there any chance?

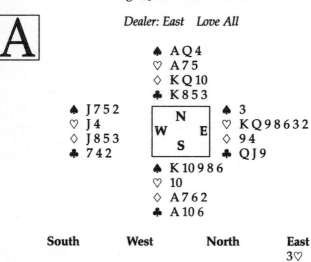

Dealer: East   Love All

♠ A Q 4
♡ A 7 5
◇ K Q 10
♣ K 8 5 3

♠ J 7 5 2
♡ J 4
◇ J 8 5 3
♣ 7 4 2

♠ 3
♡ K Q 9 8 6 3 2
◇ 9 4
♣ Q J 9

♠ K 10 9 8 6
♡ 10
◇ A 7 6 2
♣ A 10 6

South	West	North	East
			3♡
3♠	Pass	6♠	All Pass

West leads the ♡J which you win in dummy and cash the ♠A and ♠K, but East discards a heart on the second.

You appear to have two losers, one trump and one club. The club is inescapable, but there is just a chance that you might be able to 'smother' your trump loser.

You will need West to hold four diamonds and three low clubs. After the ♠K you play the ◇K, ♣A, and take a diamond finesse. The first obstacle is passed when this holds. Now cash the ◇Q, ruff a heart, and cash the ◇A discarding a heart from dummy. Finally play the ♣K and another club.

East has to win this club trick, and with only hearts left plays the ♡K. You ruff with the ♠10, and West is stymied. His ♠J is indeed smothered: either he underruffs and dummy's trump queen wins the last trick, or overruffs, only to be overruffed by dummy, allowing South's ♠9 to win the last trick.

He did have other chances (e.g. ♠A, ♠Q and later try to endplay West to lead trumps), but I think you will agree his smother play was the most artistic if not the most accurate line.

Q

Dealer: East   Game All

```
                    ♠ Q J 8 6
                    ♡ K Q
                    ◇ A K 3
                    ♣ Q 9 4 2
                  ┌─────────┐
                  │    N    │
    Lead = ♡3     │ W     E │
                  │    S    │
                  └─────────┘
                    ♠ A K 5 4 3
                    ♡ 8 5
                    ◇ 8 2
                    ♣ A K 10 7
```

South	West	North	East
			2♡ (weak)
2♠	Pass	3♡[1]	Pass
4♣[2]	Pass	4NT[3]	Pass
5♣[4]	Pass	6♠	All Pass

[1] showing spade support   [2] natural with extra values
[3] Roman Key Card Blackwood   [4] zero or three of five 'aces'

The opening lead went to East's ace and his heart return was won by dummy's king.

East's weak two might have helped you here, but then again it might have made your auction a lot more difficult.

This looks easy, so it must be time to think. Any problems?

Dealer: East   Game All

```
              ♠ Q J 8 6
              ♡ K Q
              ◇ A K 3
              ♣ Q 9 4 2
  ♠ 10 9 2         N         ♠ 7
  ♡ 7 6 3                    ♡ A J 10 9 4 2
  ◇ Q J 10 9 7 5  W   E      ◇ 6 4
  ♣ 6              S         ♣ J 8 5 3
              ♠ A K 5 4 3
              ♡ 8 5
              ◇ 8 2
              ♣ A K 10 7
```

South	West	North	East
			2♡ (weak)
2♠	Pass	3♡	Pass
4♣	Pass	4NT	Pass
5♣	Pass	6♠	All Pass

The ♡3 lead went to East's ace and his heart return was won by dummy's king.

Declarer let the side down. He drew trumps and decided that as East had shown six hearts in the bidding, West was surely more likely to hold four clubs. So he cashed the ♣AK, and was disappointed to see West show out, leaving him one trick short.

There are eleven tricks – five trumps, ◇AK, ♡K and three top clubs. You need to make the fourth club and to do this you need a 3-2 break, or to guess who holds the singleton. But is it a guess?

Always cash your outside winners on hands like this, just in case there is a hidden gem of information that removes the guess.

Draw trumps and play the ◇AK and ruff a diamond. East shows out on the third diamond, as well as having shown out on the second trump. That means that you know East's shape – one spade, six hearts (weak two) and two diamonds. That leaves four cards in clubs. So, having removed luck from the equation, you play the ♣A followed by the ♣Q and take the marked finesse for your twelfth trick.

To double or not to double, that is the question. Doubling slams can be rather dangerous – let's see how you do.

You are North at Game All in each of the following auctions.

(A)	♠ A Q 7 3	**South**	**West**	**North**	**East**
	♡ A 5 4		3♡	Double	6♡
	◇ 5 3	Pass	Pass	?	
	♣ K Q 6 2				

You have a pretty good hand and you are on lead – anything to say?

(B)	♠ –	**South**	**West**	**North**	**East**
	♡ A 7		1♠	Pass	2♡
	◇ Q J 7 5 3 2	Pass	4NT¹	Pass	5♡
	♣ J 8 6 4 2	Pass	6♡	?	
		¹ normal Blackwood			

Is this a goulash? You might have bid earlier but didn't. What now?

(C)	♠ Q J 10 6	**South**	**West**	**North**	**East**
	♡ A 7 3		1♠	Pass	2NT¹
	◇ 5 2	Pass	3♠	Pass	4NT²
	♣ 8 6 4 3	Pass	5♡³	Pass	6♠
		Pass	Pass	?	
		¹ Baron – 16+ balanced			
		² Roman Key Card Blackwood			
		³ two of five 'aces', no ♠Q			

Do you think you can handle this one?

(D)	♠ A 5 3	**South**	**West**	**North**	**East**
	♡ 7 6 5				1♣
	◇ A K 8 7 5 4	Pass	1♡	Pass	1♠
	♣ 3	Pass	4♠	Pass	6♠
		Pass	Pass	?	

Yes, you might have bid earlier but you were in a cautious mood. Anyway, sometimes by not bidding you can get your opponents where you want them.

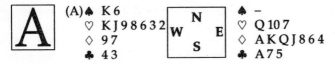

(A) ♠ K 6
♡ K J 9 8 6 3 2
◇ 9 7
♣ 4 3

♠ –
♡ Q 10 7
◇ A K Q J 8 6 4
♣ A 7 5

Obvious though it may seem, you should double and lead the ♣K. Sometimes the slam will make but because you are not quite sure what is happening you should take out insurance. Your side may well have something on in spades. You cannot afford not to double.

(B) ♠ A K Q 7 4
♡ K Q 5 4 3
◇ K 9
♣ 7

♠ J 5 2
♡ J 10 9 8 2
◇ A 8 4
♣ A 10

Partner is on lead. You want him to lead a spade, which will not be an obvious choice. Double, a Lightner Double. This asks partner to make an unusual lead. With five small spades in his hand he should not have to think too hard before making the right lead. Without the double partner is likely to lead the 'normal' ♣K.

(C) ♠ A K 9 7 5 3
♡ Q 4
◇ Q 8
♣ Q J 7

♠ 8 2
♡ K 9
◇ A K J 6 4
♣ A K 10 5

Yes, you can certainly take 6♠ off, but what about 6NT?

Always take care when doubling a slam that the opponents have nowhere else to play. 6♠ is surely going to be a good score, you do not need to double. As you can see, there are twelve easy tricks in 6NT.

(D) ♠ 10 9 8 2
♡ A K Q 10 2
◇ 9 3
♣ Q 7

♠ K Q J 7 6
♡ –
◇ 6 2
♣ A K 9 8 5 4

'Why didn't you double partner? That would have been 500 instead of just 200.' Your answer is simple: 'If I had doubled, you would have led a club expecting me to ruff it!' His face as he watched declarer pitch his diamonds would have been interesting to behold.

The moral: A slam going off is usually a good score; do not jeopardise that without good reason.

Dealer: North   Game All

Q

```
                    ♠ 3
                    ♡ A Q 7
                    ◇ A K Q 6 3
                    ♣ A Q 10 8
                       ┌─────────┐
                       │    N    │
        Lead = ◇ 10    │ W     E │
                       │    S    │
                       └─────────┘
                    ♠ A J 6 4
                    ♡ K 10 8 6 3
                    ◇ 7 5
                    ♣ 6 2
```

South	West	North	East
		1◇	Pass
1♡	Pass	3♣	Pass
3♡	Pass	4NT[1]	Pass
5♡[2]	Pass	5NT	Pass
6♡	All Pass		

[1] Roman Key Card Blackwood
[2] two of five 'aces', no trump queen

You win the ◇A, cash the ♡A all following and then the ♡Q on which West discards a club.

North could not think of anything better than Blackwood at his third turn. He received a rather desirable response. Now he continued with 5NT to show all the first-round controls and all the top trumps, but South had nothing more to say – his ♡K and ♠A were the only positive features of his hand.

The contract looks pretty good, having excellent chances even with the bad trump break. There are plenty of lines available, but which is best?

Dealer: North   Game All

```
                    ♠ 3
                    ♡ A Q 7
                    ◇ A K Q 6 3
                    ♣ A Q 10 8
        ♠ Q 9 7 5 2    ┌─────┐    ♠ K 10 8
        ♡ 5            │  N  │    ♡ J 9 4 2
        ◇ 10 2        W│     │E   ◇ J 9 8 4
        ♣ J 9 5 4 3   │  S  │    ♣ K 7
                       └─────┘
                    ♠ A J 6 4
                    ♡ K 10 8 6 3
                    ◇ 7 5
                    ♣ 6 2
```

South	West	North	East
		1◇	Pass
1♡	Pass	3♣	Pass
3♡	Pass	4NT	Pass
5♡	Pass	5NT	Pass
6♡	All Pass		

You win West's ◇ 10 lead with the ◇ A, cash the ♡ A all following and then the ♡ Q on which West discards a club.

This problem is easier than it seems. You must avoid the temptation of simply ruffing a spade in dummy. Taking the ruff leaves the spade suit wide open, as well as preventing you from picking up East's trumps.

The best line is to draw trumps, establish the diamond suit and take a double finesse in clubs. All you need for this is for West to hold one honour in clubs and the diamonds to break 4-2 or 3-3. You also make if West holds both honours, however the diamonds break.

So, draw trumps by way of the marked finesse (throwing a club on the fourth round) and then play on diamonds, ruffing the fourth round. Now play a club to the ten. East can win and switch to a spade, but you win and take your second club finesse or, as in this case, cash your top tricks.

Dealer: South   Game All

```
                    ♠ K J
                    ♡ A 7 4
                    ◇ K 10 7 2
                    ♣ K J 6 3
    ♠ Q 8 7 4      ┌─────────┐
    ♡ 6 3          │    N    │
    ◇ A J 9 4      │ W     E │
    ♣ 7 5 2        │    S    │
                   └─────────┘
```

South	West	North	East
1NT (15-17)	Pass	4NT	Pass
6NT	All Pass		

You lead the ♠4 taken by dummy's jack. Declarer continues with a club to his ace and then leads the ◇Q.

It seems that North thought their partnership was playing a stronger 'strong notrump' (16-18)!

Your lead although not disastrous has made one decision for declarer already. How do you defend?

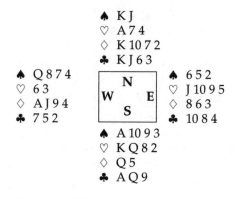

South	West	North	East
1NT (15-17)	Pass	4NT	Pass
6NT	All Pass		

West leads the ♠4 taken by dummy's jack. Declarer continues with a club to his ace and then leads the ◇Q.

This is a common situation in a slam: declarer is trying to establish an eleventh winner by losing a trick. If you win your ace and play a second spade declarer will be in control, able to test all his suits and, if necessary, all breaks being bad, he can try for a squeeze.

With chances in several suits, declarer is unlikely to put all his eggs in one basket immediately. Win the ◇A and return a diamond right away. Declarer will surely win his ◇K and play for one of the many things that may be right: hearts 3-3, the ♠Q coming down on the third round, ◇J doubleton, heart-diamond squeeze on East, heart-spade-diamond squeeze on West, etc. Unfortunately this is the hand when only the diamond finesse is right!!

If declarer guesses to finesse the diamond nothing is lost because, having tried all else, he would have fallen back on that anyway.

Had you not held the ◇J, you would do well to duck the ◇Q, because now declarer would be stuck. He is unable to test any suits, for that will give the defence a second trick to go with the ◇A. You would more or less force him to take the losing diamond finesse to partner's jack.

Dealer: North   Love All

```
          ♠ 6 3
          ♡ J 8 3
          ◇ A 7 3
          ♣ A K J 7 4
              N
Lead = ◇4   W     E
              S
          ♠ A K 8 2
          ♡ A K Q 5 4
          ◇ 9 6 2
          ♣ 10
```

South	West	North	East
		1♣	2◇ (weak)
2♡	Pass	3♡	Pass
3♠[1]	Pass	4♡	Pass
4♠[1]	Pass	4NT[2]	Pass
5♣[3]	Pass	5◇[4]	Pass
6♡[5]	All Pass		

[1] cue-bid   [2] Roman Key Card Blackwood
[3] zero or three of five 'aces'   [4] asking about the ♡Q
[5] showing the ♡Q but denying extra feature

You win the lead and cash the ♣AK. East drops the queen on the second round.

The lead is obviously a singleton. There are plenty of chances and rather than take a 50% shot with a club finesse, you hope either to establish clubs by ruffing, or take a couple of ruffs in dummy. East's ♣Q is helpful, for it clears up the situation.

What is your best line?

Dealer: North　Love All

A

```
              ♠ 6 3
              ♡ J 8 3
              ◇ A 7 3
              ♣ A K J 7 4
♠ Q J 9 7 4   ┌─────────┐   ♠ 10 5
♡ 10 9        │    N    │   ♡ 7 6 2
◇ 4          │ W     E │   ◇ K Q J 10 8 5
♣ 9 8 6 5 3   │    S    │   ♣ Q 2
              └─────────┘
              ♠ A K 8 2
              ♡ A K Q 5 4
              ◇ 9 6 2
              ♣ 10
```

South	West	North	East
		1♣	2◇ (weak)
2♡	Pass	3♡	Pass
3♠	Pass	4♡	Pass
4♠	Pass	4NT	Pass
5♣	Pass	5◇	Pass
6♡	All Pass		

You win West's ◇4 lead and cash the ♣AK. East drops the queen on the second round.

East has five cards in the majors. Consider each possibility. He will not have a five-card major because of his bid, and if he holds four hearts you have no chance. If he holds one or two hearts you could ruff one spade in dummy, cash the ♡A and ♡J and then the ♣J.

But when he holds three hearts you need two spade ruffs because you cannot cash the ♣J without drawing all the trumps. This appears impossible because you need to ruff high twice, but notice the ♡8 – it gives you the extra chance of West holding 109 doubleton.

Having won the ◇A and ♣AK, you cash the ♠AK and ruff a spade with the ♡8. If East follows you pursue the course mentioned above, but in the event he discards a diamond. So, you return to hand with a trump and ruff your last spade with the ♡J. Finally you reach hand with a club ruff to draw trumps and concede a diamond trick at the end – 6♡ made.

Dealer: South   Game All

Q

```
        ♠ 7 6 2
        ♡ J 7 3
        ◇ Q 9 5 4
        ♣ A 10 2
```

```
              N
Lead = ♠9   W   E
              S
```

```
        ♠ A K Q 5 4 3
        ♡ A K 4 2
        ◇ A
        ♣ 7 3
```

South	West	North	East
2♣	Pass	2◇	Pass
2♠	Pass	3♠	Pass
3NT[1]	Pass	5♣[2]	Pass
5◇[3]	Pass	5♠	Pass
6♠	All Pass		

[1] asking for specific aces   [2] ♣A   [3] anything extra?

You start with two rounds of trumps and find that they break 2-2.

The problem with strong hands is that most people cannot stop bidding with them!

When one hand is much stronger than the other, it is often useful to have a few asking bids and here South makes use of one – a 4♣ response to 3NT would have shown no aces with other bids showing the ace of the suit bid (responses similar to the Acol 4NT opening bid). After he had found the ♣A there was no stopping him and although North denied anything else by signing off with 5♠ that only stopped South bidding the grand!

At least the trump split has given you some hope – how do you play?

A

Dealer: South   Game All

```
                    ♠ 7 6 2
                    ♡ J 7 3
                    ◇ Q 9 5 4
                    ♣ A 10 2
   ♠ J 9                          ♠ 10 8
   ♡ 10 9 6 5      N              ♡ Q 8
   ◇ J 7 3       W   E            ◇ K 10 8 6 2
   ♣ Q 8 6 4       S              ♣ K J 9 5
                    ♠ A K Q 5 4 3
                    ♡ A K 4 2
                    ◇ A
                    ♣ 7 3
```

South	West	North	East
2♣	Pass	2◇	Pass
2♠	Pass	3♠	Pass
3NT	Pass	5♣	Pass
5◇	Pass	5♠	Pass
6♠	All Pass		

West leads the ♠9. You win and play a second round, finding that trumps break 2-2.

This really is an awful slam! So what chances do you have? Well, if you lose a heart you will have to bring down the ◇K by ruffing in order to establish the ◇Q for the club discard. How many entries do you need? Three. If the ♡Q is right (with West) you can use a heart entry (the ♡J), a trump entry and a club entry – just enough.

So, half the time you can make when one player has ◇Kxx. This does not sound very good odds. Indeed, it is not good odds and in fact the best play on this hand is the simplest play.

Cash the ♡AK and hope that the ♡Q falls. If it does you can win the ♡J and ruff your fourth heart, thus losing just one club. If it doesn't work you can still hope that the ◇K is singleton or doubleton.

This is still only about 22%, but it is the best you can get. That sums up the greatness of the slam!

Dealer: South   Game All

♠ K 6 4
♡ K Q 10
♢ K Q J 10
♣ A 4 3

♠ J 10
♡ A 5 3 2
♢ 7 2
♣ J 10 8 7 5

```
    N
 W     E
    S
```

South	West	North	East
1NT (12-14)	Pass	4NT	Pass
6NT	All Pass		

You lead the ♡ A followed by another heart.

Dummy is a point short for the normal quantitative raise, but no doubt he hoped his tens would make up for that.

Declarer wins the second trick in dummy and cashes a third heart. Then come the ♢ A and three more rounds of diamonds from dummy.

Your discards?

A

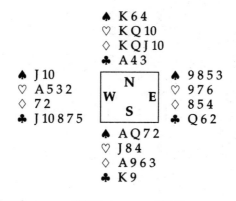

Dealer: South   Game All

	♠ K 6 4	
	♡ K Q 10	
	◇ K Q J 10	
	♣ A 4 3	

♠ J 10		♠ 9 8 5 3
♡ A 5 3 2	N	♡ 9 7 6
◇ 7 2	W E	◇ 8 5 4
♣ J 10 8 7 5	S	♣ Q 6 2

	♠ A Q 7 2	
	♡ J 8 4	
	◇ A 9 6 3	
	♣ K 9	

South	West	North	East
1NT (12-14)	Pass	4NT	Pass
6NT	All Pass		

West leads the ♡A followed by another heart. Declarer wins the
second trick in dummy and cashes a third heart. Then come the ◇A
and three more rounds of diamonds from dummy.

This is easy: you have plenty of cards and they are all pretty useless:
close your eyes and pick!

Always remember that if you hold nothing, the chances are that
partner might hold something important. Is there any information
that might help partner? You should tell him that you have clubs. At
your first discard you must play the ♣J.

East will think to himself: 'I have no particular reason for keeping
any of my cards, but if my partner holds lots of clubs, I certainly have
no reason to hold on to them.'

It is never easy to discard from Qxx. East might easily prefer to
part with a spade, after all West would have to have a doubleton
including two honours for them to be important!

Notice how you must discard the ♣J at your first opportunity,
because on the fourth diamond East has to discard before you. He
needs the vital information by that point.

With careful discarding many slams can be thwarted, but
discarding is a team effort. Try to help partner at all times.

Dealer: East   Love All

```
                        ♠ A K 4 3
                        ♡ K Q 6 2
                        ◇ 3
                        ♣ A K 9 8
                           ┌─────┐
                           │  N  │
        Lead = ◇ 5         │W   E│
                           │  S  │
                           └─────┘
                        ♠ Q 8
                        ♡ A 10 9 5
                        ◇ A K 8 6
                        ♣ 10 5 4
```

South	West	North	East
			Pass
1NT (12-14)	Pass	2♣¹	Pass
2♡	Pass	4◇²	Pass
5◇³	Pass	5NT⁴	Pass
6◇⁵	Pass	7♡	All Pass

¹ Stayman   ² splinter bid   ³ cue-bid   ⁴ grand slam force
⁵ one top honour

The opening lead fetched East's jack and declarer's ace. You play a
trump to the king, but West shows out.

North took some time over this auction, which is not too
surprising, given the prettiness of his hand, after his partner had
opened.

Can you find a line to make your slam?

Dealer: East   Love All

```
              ♠ A K 4 3
              ♡ K Q 6 2
              ◇ 3
              ♣ A K 9 8
♠ J 10 7 2         N         ♠ 9 6 5
♡ –            W       E     ♡ J 8 7 4 3
◇ Q 10 5 4 2       S         ◇ J 9 7
♣ J 7 6 3                    ♣ Q 2
              ♠ Q 8
              ♡ A 10 9 5
              ◇ A K 8 6
              ♣ 10 5 4
```

South	West	North	East
			Pass
1NT (12-14)	Pass	2♣	Pass
2♡	Pass	4◇	Pass
5◇	Pass	5NT	Pass
6◇	Pass	7♡	All Pass

The ◇5 runs to East's jack and your ace. You play a trump to the king, but West shows out.

'Don't panic!' How many tricks do you have? Four trumps (you can pick them up), three spades, two diamonds and two clubs comes to eleven tricks. You need two ruffs in dummy.

Your only possible chance is to take one small ruff, and one 'big' ruff, the latter coming when East has only trumps left and is thus forced to underruff. What shape do you need East to be?

You need one small diamond ruff, so he must have three of those; you need three spades to stand up, thus three of those; and finally he has to hold two clubs. You require East to be precisely 3-5-3-2.

After a trump to the king, play a spade to the queen and cash the ◇K. Now comes a diamond ruffed small and the ♠AK (discarding a club). East continues to follow suit. The ♣AK remove East's last non-trump cards. Next comes a club. East does best to ruff small and you overruff. Finally, the coup de grace – ruff a diamond with the ♡Q (underruffed) and finesse East's trumps for the last two tricks. Wow!

Dealer: South   Game All

```
            ♠ A K 7 2
            ♡ A K 9
            ◇ 10 5
            ♣ Q 6 3 2
                 N
Lead: ♡Q    W       E
                 S
            ♠ Q J 10
            ♡ 7 5 3
            ◇ A J 6
            ♣ A K J 10
```

South	West	North	East
1NT (15-17)	Pass	2♣	Pass
2◇	Pass	4NT	Pass
6NT	All Pass		

A nice and easy auction, with South judging his 'good 16' to be enough to take the push to slam.

Unfortunately, you appear to be a trick short and there do not appear to be many available paths. Can you find a way to twelve tricks?

A

Dealer: South   Game All

```
              ♠ A K 7 2
              ♡ A K 9
              ♢ 10 5
              ♣ Q 6 3 2
 ♠ 8 5                        ♠ 9 6 4 3
 ♡ Q J 10 4      N           ♡ 8 6 2
 ♢ Q 9 4 3    W     E        ♢ K 8 7 2
 ♣ 9 8 5         S           ♣ 7 4
              ♠ Q J 10
              ♡ 7 5 3
              ♢ A J 6
              ♣ A K J 10
```

South	West	North	East
1NT (15-17)	Pass	2♣	Pass
2♢	Pass	4NT	Pass
6NT	All Pass		

West leads the ♡Q.

West is highly likely to hold the sole heart guard because the ♡Q lead from QJxx would be quite risky.

You might play East to hold the ♢KQ but that is poor odds. Instead, it is better to play for split honours in diamonds, and assume that West does have the only heart guard.

Win the ♡A, cross to hand and play a small diamond towards the ten. If West rises with an honour, you finesse East for the other. More likely, West will let the diamond run to his partner. Now you prepare to squeeze West in the red suits.

On a diamond return you win the ♢A, cash four spades (throwing a heart) and then four clubs finishing in hand. On the last club West can keep only two of the ♡J10 and ♢Q and thus has to cede the twelfth trick in whichever suit he decides to discard from.

On a heart return the play is similar except that you have to play the squeeze card from dummy, i.e. you play similarly except that you win the fourth club in dummy. West is squeezed in the same way but this time he has to keep two of the ♡J and ♢Q9, and you have your entries in the right place.

Dealer: East   Love All

```
              ♠ A
              ♡ 8 6
              ◇ A Q 10 9 4
              ♣ A K Q J 3
                 ┌─────────┐
                 │    N    │
Lead: ♡K         │ W     E │
                 │    S    │
                 └─────────┘
              ♠ 7 6 4
              ♡ A
              ◇ 5 3 2
              ♣ 10 9 8 6 4 2
```

South	West	North	East
			1♠
Pass	4♡	4NT (minors)	Double
5♣	Pass	6♣	Double
All Pass			

With your solitary ace, you were not looking forward to this contract, but then you did not expect partner to put down a shapely 20-count! North's 6♣ was optimistic, but he hoped that with nothing his partner would have passed the double of 4NT back to him. Well, can you reward your partner's faith in your declarer play?

A

Dealer: East   Love All

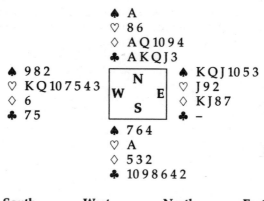

```
                    ♠ A
                    ♡ 8 6
                    ◇ A Q 10 9 4
                    ♣ A K Q J 3
  ♠ 9 8 2                          ♠ K Q J 10 5 3
  ♡ K Q 10 7 5 4 3      N          ♡ J 9 2
  ◇ 6              W         E      ◇ K J 8 7
  ♣ 7 5                 S          ♣ —
                    ♠ 7 6 4
                    ♡ A
                    ◇ 5 3 2
                    ♣ 10 9 8 6 4 2
```

South	West	North	East
			1♠
Pass	4♡	4NT	Double
5♣	Pass	6♣	Double
All Pass			

West leads the ♡K.

With West having the ♡K and most likely the ♡Q, it looks as if both diamond honours could well be wrong (certainly the king). Can you still make your slam?

Basically, you require an endplay, but are there enough entries?

Try it out: win the ♡A, cash the ♠A, ruff a heart high, ruff a spade high, play a club to hand and ruff your last spade high. One more club to draw the outstanding trump, but you are in the wrong hand.

In fact, it does not matter which hand you are in. Your plan is to play the ◇Q and let East win his king, leaving him endplayed. So that is exactly what you do.

Having eliminated the majors as above, you exit with the ◇Q. If East ducks this, you lose just one diamond trick and make your game. If he wins it he is endplayed: a major suit return gives a ruff and discard (you throw your last losing diamond from hand); a diamond return runs round to dummy's tenace.

Not quite the contract you predicted when you picked up your hand, but well played nevertheless!

Solve the clues beneath the diagram (some are letters and some numbers), revealing the hand and the bidding. Then all you need do is solve the problem. (Note: ten and double are abbreviated differently than in the rest of the book.)

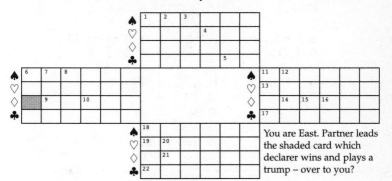

You are East. Partner leads the shaded card which declarer wins and plays a trump – over to you?

	S		W		N		E	
23	24	25	26	27	28*	29	30	
31								

* small piece of wood

(Across and Down clues listed together)

1 Roman water
2 6.55
3 74 squares
4 A solid V
5 Moysian

6 Line up to see the bird
7 Start of the second
8 This number and four more
9 This question
10 Unlucky for Australians?

11 Without the club jack
12 After the tie is broken
13 From Holyhead to Shrewsbury
14 1 more than 15
15 Steps
16 Bishop's degree
17 Bigger than Bond

18 Dog tooth
19 Signed the Magna Carta
20 East's spades with food already inside
21 One year before William came
22 One less than 18

23 How the Australians would say '5 for 1'
24 Three hearts. Two English, one French
25 Pub
26 Antimony and Boron
27 Three boundaries in a row
28 Bad shovels contain this
29 Norwegian Knight on the Queen's rank
30 Very dark pencil
31 Nobody fails

A

```
              ♠ A 5 4
              ♡ Q T 9 3
              ◇ V O I D
              ♣ A 7 6 5 4 3
♠ Q T 8 3 2   ┌─────────┐   ♠ J 7 6
♡ 4 2         │    N    │   ♡ A 5
◇ A Q 9 8 7   │ W     E │   ◇ K 4 3 2
♣ J           │    S    │   ♣ Q T 9 2
              └─────────┘
              ♠ K 9
              ♡ K J 8 7 6
              ◇ J T 6 5
              ♣ K 8
```

S	W	N	E
1 H	1 S	4 D*	N B
4 H	N B	4 S	N B
5 C	N B	6 H	D B
All Pass			

* splinter

Lead: ◇ A. Declarer ruffs and plays a trump.

Had partner led his singleton club this slam would have had no chance, but even with the diamond lead you should be able to take declarer down.

Whether you win the first or the second trump you must continue with a diamond. This cuts down the entries to dummy and stops declarer enjoying dummy's clubs. (Declarer needs three entries – he has one in clubs and one in spades, but once you play a second diamond he loses his third entry, in trumps.)

But if you win the first trump and play a low diamond (the ◇ K would allow declarer to take a ruffing finesse against West), this leaves you controlling both minors, which will cause problems later. Declarer will ruff the ◇ Q in dummy, cross to the ♠ K and ruff another diamond. Now the ♠ A and ♡ K allow declarer to draw trumps and at the same time squeeze you in the minors.

So, to avoid this less than graceful end, you must duck the trump lead. If declarer continues trumps you should win and play a diamond. Whatever declarer does after you duck he cannot make twelve tricks.